Children with Language Disabilities

Children with Language Disabilities

Michael Beveridge
and
Gina Conti-Ramsden

OPEN UNIVERSITY PRESS

Milton Keynes · Philadelphia

Open University Press
Celtic Court
22 Ballmoor
Buckingham MK18 1XH

and
1900 Frost Road, Suite 101
Bristol, PA 19007, USA

First published 1987
Reprinted 1990

Copyright © 1987 Michael Beveridge and Gina Conti-
Ramsden

British Library Cataloguing in Publication Data

Beveridge, Michael
 Children with language disabilities.
 1. Language disorders in children
 I. Title   II. Conti-Ramsden, Gina
618.92'855   RJ496.L35

ISBN 0 335 10280 8
ISBN 0 335 10279 4 Pbk

Library of Congress Cataloging-in-Publication Data

Beveridge, Michael.
 Children with language disabilities.
 1. Learning disabled children — Language. 2. Learning
 disabled children — Education — Language arts.   3. Oral
 communication — Study and teaching.   I. Conti–Ramsden,
 Gina.   II. Title.
LC4704.5.B48   1987   371.91'4   87–5779

ISBN 0 335 10280 8
ISBN 0 335 10279 4 Pbk

Text design by Clarke Williams

Printed in Great Britain by J.W. Arrowsmith Ltd., Bristol

For Jorge and Alicia Conti.
For Skippy.

Contents

Acknowledgements

We would like to acknowledge the helpful comments of Elspeth McCartney, Ann Neville, Margaret Gunn and Dorothy Bishop; the co-operation of the staff of Liverpool Speech Therapy Services, the language teachers, the children with whom we have worked and also Hilda Proctor who typed the manuscript.

About the Authors

Professor Michael Beveridge has worked in speech pathology departments and at the Hester Adrian Research Centre and is now the Chair of Education Department, University of Bristol. He has published extensively on the communication problems of children with special needs and has produced several books on aspects of children's language. His current research is into ways of understanding the development of literacy skills. Dr Beveridge has a particular interest in the ways that pictures and diagrams can help understanding, and his most recent papers on this topic appear in *Memory and Cognition* and the *Journal of Research in Reading*.

Dr Gina Conti-Ramsden is a qualified speech therapist who lectures in language development and disabilities in the Centre for Educational Guidance and Special Needs, School of Education at the University of Manchester. After studying at Hamilton College, New York, and the University of Cambridge, England, she took a PhD in communication disorders at the University of Texas. She has worked with language-disabled children in schools as well as language units and has published a variety of research articles and books on language problems. She has also spent 2 years as a Visiting Scholar at Harvard University's Graduate School of Education.

1

Introduction

A young infant teacher begins a discussion during a workshop on language disabilities by saying:

> I have been waiting for this session with great interest because I feel I am not communicating with some of the children in my classroom. Take, for example, Tim . . . he is bright, follows instructions, relates well to the other children in the classroom, but I can hardly understand what he says when he talks to me. They seem to understand him . . . the other children in the class I mean . . . but, I can't. Well, I can but not always and it is hard work trying to guess what he is trying to say. His sentences are rather short and they get shorter the more I ask him to repeat, so I don't think I'm doing him any good by asking him, 'What was that, Tim?' What do you think? Does anybody else have children like that?

A primary teacher continued:

> I have come across those children many times before. They all speak with funny accents one cannot possibly understand. Many of them come from homes where their parents only use simple language . . . so, what do you expect the child to do?

Another teacher enters the discussion. She taught Class 4 in a primary school.

> I can see your problem with Tim and other children like him, but at least he understands! I have two children in my class who both have trouble following what I say or when I read a story. Joshua is still the most distractible child I have ever met. One would have thought that he would have 'grown out' of this but he hasn't. The number of times I have to repeat things to him! It makes me wonder why it is that I am doing that lesson! Joshua does not always understand what is

said to him despite the fact that he can talk properly . . . I mean his sentences are not very complex, but I certainly don't have trouble understanding what he says. And neither do I have trouble with Alex. He is very clear, and his attention is not bad. But, oftentimes he looks at me rather puzzled when I ask him why or how questions after a story we have read·. . . he is more of a puzzle than Alex.

'If you want a puzzle you should meet Paddy, one of my students', said a secondary teacher:

Give Paddy some work and he'll sit and get on with it. But, that is his problem. He sits quietly and gets on with things. He has no friends . . . I know he is usually on his own at break times. When I try to have a conversation with Paddy, I have to do all the work! I ask all the questions. He never starts a conversation himself, he doesn't always look at you when you talk to him . . . he doesn't really know how to interact with people. And this is not just at school. I have spoken at various times with his parents and it is the same at home. He is also very literal. Tell Paddy to go and jump out of the window and he probably would! He doesn't go beyond what is said, he can't read between the lines. One good example is his sense of humour, or should I say his lack of one. He never laughs with the rest of the class. It is as if he doesn't see what was funny. I think all these things go back to using language and communicating with people. Do you think that could be a language problem?

This book is for teachers like these who try to understand and help language-disabled children day in and day out. Children learn language in order to communicate with other people and to organise and learn about their world. Those children who fail to learn their native language normally may be adversely affected in their social development, their emotional adjustment and the cognitive and academic achievement. These language-disabled children require help from a variety of professionals: teachers, speech therapists, psychologists.

The two professional groups which are most experienced in the teaching of language-disabled children are speech therapists and the staff of the few special schools for these children. The aim of this book is to draw together some of the basic principles and practices evolved in these contexts. We attempt to do this in a way which can contribute to the understanding of language-disabled children whose main help will come from teachers of special needs in ordinary schools. This orientation means we say little about a curriculum design for the language disabled. In normal schools their curriculum will be integrated into the overall school programme. Furthermore, the children themselves will typically have less severe language difficulties than those who are in special schools. We intend to highlight problems and remedial principles which can operate within the normal school setting. However, there are some features of an overall language curriculum for the more severely disabled which may prove useful to special-needs teachers.

We recommend Ella Hutt's book on this topic for more detailed information from a very experienced teacher. And for those teachers who may face younger children with severe language problems in nursery units, we suggest the book by Jenny Warner and her colleagues (see Further Reading). These teacher-researchers give many helpful examples of good educational practice based on well-founded principles, which we will now briefly outline.

Language as part of a wider system of symbolic representation

It is now part of the folklore of child psychology that we cannot fully understand the emergence of language skills without looking at the other ways children make one object or action stand for another. This process of the development of symbolic thought integrates play, mime, gesture, speech, drawing, speaking, reading and writing into activities of which we can ask, 'What does this *mean* to the child?' The child develops relationships between written words and real objects in the world, between miniature toys and real people, between a line sketch of an animal and the real animal, and so on. In this way the child develops meaning and symbolic understanding. This is why the parrot's mimicry is not language, because it means nothing to the parrot; also, this is why echolalic phrases of autistic children are not considered language or communication.

The principle of language as part of this wider system of

symbolic representation tells us that we can develop the child's understanding of meaning relations through non-linguistic techniques. We can expect improvements in those aspects of language disability which we have earlier discussed as related to the child's appreciation of important *contrasts* in meaning if we can insert our language work into relevant play, drawing, gesture, and so on. When doing so it is very important to bear in mind that associating one symbol with another does not necessarily show that the child knows what *either* of them mean. We must be very careful when associating words with pictures, initiated activities or gestures. The child may simply be putting two events together in the way the behaviourist B.F. Skinner has shown to be possible for almost any pair of stimuli, both of which may mean very little to the child. For example, when young children are taught to wave bye-bye before they have any understanding of the consequences of absence or presence of people, they are learning a response which is for them quite meaningless. The children need an anchor on one of the objects or events before they can relate it to another object or event.

The hierarchy of learning

Many psychologists since William James in the last century have produced hierarchies of learning processes. In this book we work within a system which is compatible with most of those theoretical edifices as well as with established principles of good teaching.

We have distinguished between problems of attention, perception, meaning, memory and organisation. We have shown that children can have difficulties with language at all these levels, and furthermore that attempts to resolve difficulties at the higher levels (e.g. organisation) have, as a prerequisite, skill at the lower levels (e.g. attention). As we illustrate, good curriculum planning must include provision both for the level of learning process that the child finds problematic and for ways of taking him further up the hierarchy.

Language and the expressive arts

Our focus in this book is on the processes of language itself and we say little about how general skills of self-expression can be developed. Curriculum planning should of course include drama, music, art and craft as essential ingredients of language teaching. Drama is the time-honoured mode of access to the world of feelings. It is particularly important for children whose access to literature is likely to be limited.

Music has a special role for some language-disabled children because of the parallel between its organisation of pitch and rhythm and the way intonation and stress operate in normal speech. Tasks of musical pitch and rhythm discrimination can be given similar to those we have discussed with reference to speech sounds. The visual representation of high versus low notes, long versus short notes, and loud versus soft notes is another way of assisting children to perceive these contrasts. Tunes can also be illustrated using different colours, shades and sizes to represent types of notes. Those children with sound sequencing difficulties are most likely to benefit from this approach.

Art and craft skills are useful for two reasons. First, language-disabled children can also have problems in the co-ordination of physical action. Second, those aspects of the curriculum can be very useful in providing a knowledge base for language teaching to use as subject-matter.

In general, then, we must look for all ways of encouraging communication skills through the expressive arts. But this must occur around a thorough assessment of the language problems faced by each child.

All communicative interactions, be they oral, written, signs or gestures, involve language. However, in this book we are using the term 'language' to refer mainly to oral language. Our use of the term 'language disabilities' refers primarily to problems in the production and comprehension of speech and how these link with difficulties in acquiring literacy skills. For reasons of both unity of purpose and available space, the problems of bilingualism and other cultural differences are not part of the focus of this book. However, see Further Reading towards the end of the book for some useful current references on these topics. The topic of stammering is also too vast to be included, but a few basic references to fluency problems are also included.

The book is made up of nine chapters. Following this introductory chapter, Chapter 2 provides a general outline of the stages involved in language development. The child is seen as a complex biological mechanism within a complex social context from which communication arises. Chapter 3 examines three important factors which influence the child's language proficiency: the language environment, the hearing ability of the child an the child's neurology. Chapter 4 describes the SCORE model for language teaching. This model contains five principles which provide a framework for helping children with language disabilities. This framework is applied throughout the remainder of the book.

Chapters 5 to 7 characterise the problems of children with language disabilities. Chapter 5 discusses speech sound problems, including dysarthria, dyspraxia and phonological difficulties. Chapter 6 looks at children's problems when organising words into language. The chapter covers problems of production as well as comprehension, conceptual/verbal reasoning problems, memory and attentional difficulties. It also discusses a variety of useful approaches to help children with grammatical disabilities. Chapter 7 provides a general background to the use of language for social interaction and discusses the problems experienced by conversationally disabled children.

Language, the school and literacy are discussed in Chapters 8 and 9. Chapter 8 looks at the school organisation and its impact on language disabilities. It also provides the reader with guidelines for the identification of children with potential language difficulties. Chapter 9 presents a model of literacy which links the child's oral problems with those of reading and writing. The model suggests that the teaching of literacy can be turned to the advantage of children with spoken-language disabilities.

Conclusion

This short chapter suggests that the specific language-teaching techniques discussed in this book can be integrated into an overall curriculum according to principles which see language as (1) part of a wider symbolic system, (2) subject to a hierarchy of learning processes and (3) related to traditional modes of expression found in the school curriculum. All three principles of integration are important if children are to make lasting progress in communicating.

This book is aimed at helping teachers to become better acquainted with the full range of language disabilities. As professionals in the midst of much development in research and practice, teachers are required to take a multidisciplinary approach and to take more and more responsibility for identifying, referring and teaching children with special needs.

2

Language Development:
How Does It Happen?

Language is for meeting people, making social relationships, for interacting with others and for forming and expressing our thoughts. Language is our most precious interactive ingredient, but how do the child's skills develop?

Starting to use language

Almost from birth the baby begins the process of learning how to socialise. He soon finds out that if he smiles at his mother she will smile back; if he makes a noise to his father, dad will make one too. He learns that his actions can influence people, that what he does can cause other people to do something in response. Gradually, the baby and those very close to him (usually mother and father) develop a series of gamelike shared routines. For example, they may engage in routines such as the baby making a gurgling noise, the mother saying something to him, the baby gurgling again, and so on. In this way the child begins to learn how to take his turn in social exchanges.

But what sparks off this interest in interaction? Is it genetically predetermined or is it the environment that shows the child what to do? In fact both are very important. Human beings have evolved as social animals, and the young child is biologically prepared to seek social interaction and to follow social patterns. But the people involved in shared exchanges with the young child, and in the setting in which these interactions occur, are also very important. Thus the current view is that the social bases for language acquisition begin to develop soon after birth and both nature (the child's genetic endowment) and nurture (the child's environment) have a crucial role to play in laying the social foundations for language use.

One of the most striking illustrations that young babies are actively social has been provided by Colwyn Trevarthen at the University of Edinburgh. He allowed mothers and babies to play turn-taking exchange games involving cooing, smiling, and so on. However, the situation Trevarthen studied was unusual because the mother and the baby were each placed in front of a different TV camera. This relayed the facial expressions and noises of each to the other via a TV screen. Typically, these routines will go on for some minutes, with the babies taking great pleasure in them.

The use of the TV apparatus allowed Trevarthen to take a video recording of exactly what the baby sees the mother doing during each series of exchanges. The interesting and important finding was that when these pictures of their mothers were replayed to the babies they become very agitated and often show signs of distress. The crucial difference in this second encounter is that the mother's behaviour, while identical with that which initially gave pleasure, is not now truly interactive. It goes on regardless of the babies' responses, like a conversation where one person does not listen. Hence it is not just mother's face, smiles and noises which babies enjoy, it is the full participation in these early 'conversations'. The baby must feel part of a relationship even at this young age. These social encounters provide a foundation for the emergence of language.

Within the context of early interactions, the baby uses gestures, activities and sounds which are interpreted as intentionally having particular meaning: when the baby grunts the mother may say, 'Oh! he wants me to pick him up'; or when the baby whines the father may say, 'Oh, you did not like that, did you?' Slowly, the baby begins to associate certain sounds with certain routines. In this stage also several important prerequisites occur in preparation for later phonological (sound system) development. The ability of the infant to discriminate perceptually between different speech sounds develops and the child begins to engage in 'sound play'. This babbling sound play becomes increasingly speech like. The child begins to organise this vocalisation into basic rhythm/pitch units which form the basis of later intonation and the transition from vocalisation to the use of the child's first words (e.g. mama, dada).

The child's first words show what he is interested in, and that usually involves actions and people or objects. He learns the names of those people who are important in his life – 'mummy' and 'daddy'. Food is important, so he will learn to say 'milk' and 'nana'; animals, clothes and toys also feature in the infant vocabulary. Actions also engage the child's attention; he may say 'up' when he wants to be picked up, or 'gone' when he sees his mother leaving the room. And as would be expected the child only uses these words in a way which refers to his 'here and now'.

At the one-word stage of development the child has mastered one key idea about language. He has learned that a particular combination of sounds (e.g. cake) refers to a particular object in the world. This has been possible not only through a conducive environment for language learning but also because his oral mechanism has matured enough to allow him to put certain sequences of sounds together. As we will see later in this book, some children encounter difficulties in this aspect of language development (see Ch. 5).

From what has been said so far it will be clear that it is difficult to say exactly when a child starts to use language. It is hard to look at babbling gradually evolving into speech and decide when 'language' has truly begun. Parents usually identify the beginning of language use from the first words they can recognise in their child's speech. Unfortunately, the business of recognising a child's first word depends on the parents' perceptions, skills and imagination, so even here there is no agreement. We suggest that language development is a gradual process which more than likely originates at birth.

In recent years research into language acquisition has led to the rejection of the idea that there is a 'normal' language for each age. Currently, we take a view of language development as being by stages which children can go through at different rates and in different ways. Even at the one-word stage, where children predominantly use one-word utterances, there are already differences in age and the type of words used. Some children tend to be namers of objects (doggie, juice, car) while others tend to be more interested in social routines (hello, bye-bye, stop-it). These styles are not absolute; some children are both namers and are social. Also, children may change their styles across time; they may begin by being mostly social and then concentrate on naming and vice versa.

In this book, although ages are mentioned from time to time, they are not meant to imply a precise age-related model of language development which 'normal' children follow; rather they are used to illustrate particular case examples and thus give the reader a flavour of the sort of child we are talking about. The remainder of this chapter illustrates further stages of language development. This is important because we know that all children follow the *same* stages in the *same* order. What we cannot emphasise enough is that there are great individual differences in children as to the pace and the way they go through them.

Starting to use utterances

The young child has ahead of him the task of learning that words are organised in special ways and are not just randomly put together. In due course he has to know and use this complex system without effort. At the one-word stage of development the child has little opportunity to organise utterances, although early attempts to express basic needs and ideas may be evident. The child may try to connect single words together in some kind of sequence. He may say 'mummy. mummy. up.' when he wants to be picked up. From the intonation pattern we know that words are not combined together, they are still separate items. But gradually the child begins to put two words together, and when this happens a new set of doors open for the child. The two-word stage presents the child with a better opportunity to express meaning and ideas. As we will see later in this book, some children have difficulty in this area. They have difficulty in learning how words are organised together to express ideas (see Ch. 6).

When the child uses two-word utterances he continues to

use language to meet people, develop relationships and interactions, but he now has a more effective tool available to him. He can now attract the attention of others by saying 'look doggie', 'see daddy'. He can mark possession – 'mummy sock', 'Danny nose'; disappearance – 'allgone milk'; negation – 'no baby'; recurrence or the return of something missing – 'more cheese'; attribution – 'dirty sock'; existence – 'that horsie'; and many other ideas. He also uses what he has to the fullest extent by using the same two-word combination to mean very different things depending on the context. For example, 'Mummy juice' may mean 'mummy's juice' if the child points to mummy's glass of orange on the table, but it may mean 'mummy, give me some juice' if the child points to the refrigerator where the juice is kept.

The growing use of utterances

As the child becomes more proficient in language, he becomes aware of two important principles: first, that language can be used to do many things: to relate to people, to get what one wants, to lie, to joke, to please, to hurt, and so on; second, that language is organised in a systematic, rule-governed way. It is not unusual to hear a child add 'ed' to all verbs to form a past tense. He will say 'hurted, goed, hided'; words which he has never heard. He will also say 'my feets' and 'more big'. This type of 'mistake' gives us a clue as to what the child is doing. He is not learning one item at a time but instead he is formulating rules as to how the language system is organised. The more complex his sentences get, the more aware the child must be of the rules governing those utterances and the more chances the child has to do more things with language.

After the two-word stage there is a gradual increase in complexity of the child's system. The child will begin to use multi-word utterances, such as 'the toy is new'. He will also acquire rules for forming other types of utterances, such as questions: 'Is that my toy?' During this period, between 3 and 5 years of age approximately, the child is constantly deriving rules as to how the language system works.

Language development after the age of 5 involves both the

learning of new things and doing old things better. The 'mistakes' we have talked about will disappear. The child will no longer come and say, 'I hurted myself' but will correctly use both regular and irregular verbs in the past tense, he will join sentences together with 'and', 'but' and 'because'; he will also form complex negative sentences appropriately, such as 'I *don't* want to sleep *any* more'.

In order to learn more about the language of children older than 5 we have to do more than just listen to the way they talk. We need to organise tasks and situations which allow us to detect the gaps in their linguistic knowledge. We said that by 5 the child has learned much about word order. He can handle utterances such as 'Postman Pat brought the letter' and 'Did Postman Pat bring the letter?' But he cannot always handle utterances like 'The boy the cat scratched was riding a horse'. If you ask him, 'Who did the cat scratch?' he may very well say, 'The horse'. This is because the word order in these type of utterances is more complicated than it seems. Although the 'horse' comes after 'scratched', it is the boy that was scratched and not the horse. The young child will use all he knows and his common sense to try to interpret these utterances, but if the situation and common sense does not help him, he will not understand. The utterances show us that the child still has a lot to learn at this stage. (For more details of the type of strategies children use to interpret complex sentences, see Ch. 6).

A hint as to the way primary-school children organise meanings is given by word association games. If you say to a child 'blue', he will probably say 'sky', whereas an adult will probably say 'red' or another colour. In the case of the child, he tries to associate words that go together in sentences such as 'blue sky'. The child is trying to *connect* words together. The adult, on the other hand, gives an alternative word from the same semantic category. The adult is trying to *group* words together.

Conclusion

We have seen that language development involves change from one stage to another where language use, understanding and interaction all go hand in hand. The young newborn child is a complex biological mechanism within a complex social context; together they mature, interact and influence development. This development involves an ordered sequence of stages, each progressively more complex. Children go through these stages at very different rates and exhibiting a variety of styles and individual differences.

From these early stages it is evident that the structure (grammar) of the language is intimately related to the meanings conveyed by language. When we discuss language-disabled children we must keep this in mind as there is a constant temptation to think of each problem as fitting into a neat separate category such as 'word meaning' or 'grammar'. And children whose main difficulty is understanding language will typically also have problems putting words together to express themselves. It is important also to continue to acknowledge existing individual differences among children. Research in second language learning has given use some idea as to the relevant factors involved in individual differences in language learning. Global characteristics of the children such as personality, social competence and communicative preferences play a role. We shall see that some children have problems in these areas and thus fail to be able to use language to communicate (see Ch. 7).

There will be differences between the degree of skill children bring to language learning. Differences in children's memory, verbal reasoning abilities, inferential abilities and verbal playfulness are important. And as we shall see, some language-disabled children may have quite severe difficulties in one or more of these areas.

3

Understanding the Background of Language Disabilities

This chapter examines the most important factors which influence children's language proficiency. Because children get the key to their language through both speech directed to them and speech going on around them, we will look at the effects of this language environment. Does the language children hear contribute to the presence of language disability? Another factor which can influence the way children's language develops is their ability to hear their language environment correctly. Consequently the effect of hearing loss is also discussed in this chapter. Finally, because it is known that language impairment may be associated with damage to the child's brain, the role of the brain in language processing is outlined.

The language they hear

Although there has been much debate about the precise relationship between education and language, it is clear that the child's language system is a key factor in his educational success or failure. The language that surrounds the child at home will determine which language the child speaks: English children speak English while French children speak French. It will also determine the sort of accent children have, the way they speak. The question then arises of whether or not the language that surrounds language-disabled children is appropriate: is it inappropriate and thus a causal factor in the children's language problem?

How mothers talk to their children

It is known that when mothers, other adults and older children talk to young children they do so in a special way. Their sentences are shorter and simpler, they speak slower and clearer, and they exaggerate their intonation. This special way of talking to young children has been called *motherese*, and it is thought that motherese helps the child to learn language.

Many researchers have tried to find differences in the way mothers speak to their language-disabled children in the hope of finding clues about the causes of children's language problems. But the clues to language disability are *not* in the language the child hears at home. In general, mothers of language-disabled children use motherese in the same way mothers of other young children do. Language-disabled children are usually surrounded by talk which is very similar to that heard by young, normal language-learning children. Both are usually presented with similar opportunities to learn language. None the less, it is important to acknowledge that there are exceptions. Some families may provide a more suitable environment than others, and this may have repercussions as to how children cope with language. For example, there may be a mismatch within the family unit as to the styles of talk. A very reticent mother who hardly speaks to anyone may not be a suitable match for a language-disabled child with grammatical difficulties. Such a child needs a great deal of practice of putting words together, which may not be available in such an environment. In these cases intervention with the mother–child dyad is necessary to try to change the mother's and the child's styles so that they may match more closely.

Language development and social class

It is known that on average, working-class children obtain lower scores than middle-class children on tests of IQ and language development. This finding has led educationalists and researchers to suggest that this difference in performance is due to the working-class children's homes. They argue that the working-class mothers do not talk frequently to their children and thus deprive them of opportunities to learn language. By the time the children come to school, they have deficient language and cannot cope with the learning that is required.

Surprisingly, those who argue this position have not gone to working-class homes and checked whether children are indeed linguistically deprived. They have, instead, assumed that this is the case. Barbara Tizard and Martin Hughes and also Gordon Wells have tried to remedy this situation by going to working-class children's homes and recording the conversations between mothers and their children. Their results show that working-class 'language deprivation' is a myth and not a reality. Mothers of working-class children talk as much to their children, they use as many questions and controlling remarks as mothers of middle-class children do. This is not to say that there are no differences in the styles of talking and interacting at all. It is known that children themselves are very different from each other: some are talkative, some are very quiet. There are also differences between mothers, and styles also differ among social classes. It is known, for example, that working-class mothers tend to talk more about family, household and domestic topics to their children than middle-class mothers do. In addition, they more often play exciting physical games with their children than middle-class mothers do. Again, these are generalisations, and we cannot emphasise enough the vast individual differences that exist. What we must not lose sight of is the fact that these differences are not the cause of working-class children's difficulties at school. Working-class children receive as many opportunities to learn language in their working-class homes as middle-class children receive in their middle-class homes.

However, mismatches can arise when working-class children go to school. If these children are used to a certain style of interaction and talk at home and then they go to school and are expected to engage in a different style of interaction and task, let's say a more middle-class style, then there may be difficulties. A gap of many types can exist between what the child is used to at home and what the child is expected to do at school. At the level of action, playing with water or making footprints in nursery school usually invite punishment in the children's home but are encouraged in most nursery schools. At the linguistic level many words take on a technical meaning in school, for example vacuum, evaporation. Most teachers actively attempt to bridge the gap between school and home by visiting the children at home, having parents spend time in school and by sending diaries back and forth from school to home and back where information about activities is shared.

Different types of language

A quick tour around places such as Birmingham, East London, Liverpool and Newcastle brings to our attention the fact that there are many ways of speaking English in Britain. But are some ways of speaking English better than others? Are some children *disadvantaged* because they hear certain dialects of English?

It is fully accepted that no language or dialect is inherently inferior (or superior) to any other. Furthermore, all dialects and languages are suited to the needs of the community that uses them. Thus English does not need many different words for the colour green (which Amazonian Indian languages have) or many different words for snow (which Eskimo has). None the less, it is important to take into account people's attitudes towards different dialects. We have all heard comments such as 'He uses bad English', 'He is too lazy to put aitches in his words', 'He can't talk properly', as well as comments such as 'The Queen's English', 'She has a beautiful rich accent'. These comments reflect the bias of our society to prefer dialects which reflect the social prestige of their speakers. What is important is to distinguish our attitudes towards different dialects as opposed to the inherent properties of the dialects themselves. The Queen's English is not inherently better than Liverpool Scouse, but unfortunately, some people's attitudes make it clear that they prefer the former rather than the latter. Thus children who speak certain dialects of English are not *linguistically* disadvantaged in the sense that their dialects are as adequate as any other for communication. But, unfortunately, they are disadvantaged in the sense that our attitude towards their dialects use can often be negative. They can also be disadvantaged if they cannot easily communicate with Standard English or other dialect speakers. For example, some sort of uniformity of speech is necessary in the classroom. Teachers then have the difficult task of accepting the children's dialects but at the same time encouraging them to learn Standard English.

The impact of hearing on language and education

Centuries ago, Aristotle wrote, 'the ear is the organ of education'. Certainly, normal hearing is of vital importance to the development of language and thus to education.

The young, hearing child is constantly stimulated by sounds, cars passing by, mother's voice, the cat meowing. In contrast, there is the confusing world of the partially hearing children – for some the world is silent, for others it speaks but is not always clear or loud enough. Hearing impairment is not something you either have or don't have. It is a matter of degree. But, what do we mean when we say it is a matter of degree? Let's hear the world around us. There are loud sounds, soft sounds, high-pitched sounds and low-pitched sounds. Figure 3.1 attempts to map the different sounds we hear.

Children's hearing can be affected at any level shown in Figure 3.1. Thus some children may not be able to hear soft sounds like the rustling of leaves or the sound of the sea. But we must not forget there is another dimension to hearing – that is, pitch. Some sounds are high-pitched, like a whistle, and some are low-pitched, like a motor running. Thus children may have difficulties with soft sounds, but their difficulties may vary depending on pitch. That is to say, they may be better able to hear low-pitched soft sounds, such as a car starting, than high-pitched soft sounds of our language, like *f*, *th* and *s*. Other children may be worse off. They may only hear medium to loud sounds of different pitches. For these children a baby crying may be a very soft sound indeed. Well, what does this mean? Look above 'baby crying' in Figure 3.1. They are missing *all* the sounds that make up language! Some children can hear even less. For these children the lawn-mower may be a faint sound. This means they are missing all that goes above 'lawn-mower' in the diagram: the dog barking, the telephone ringing, people speaking. We can draw lines across the diagram at any level,

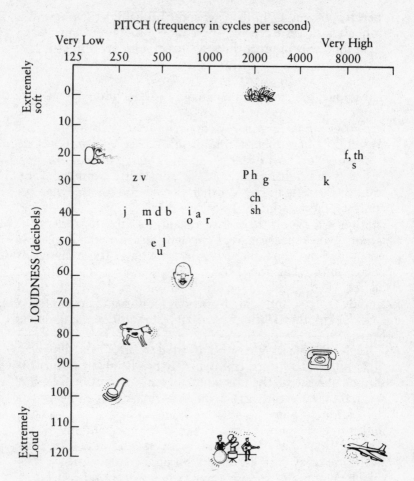

Figure 3.1 Examples of sounds at different levels of pitch and loudness

erase everything above that line, look at what has been rubbed off and this represents what the child is missing. In this way we can begin to understand what different degrees of hearing difficulties mean.

It is also important to remember what we said about pitch. Hearing problems do not usually affect all pitches equally. So a 'naughty' child who can hear a dog barking outside the school window but does not pay attention to what you say, especially words with *f*, *th* and *s* sounds, could be partially

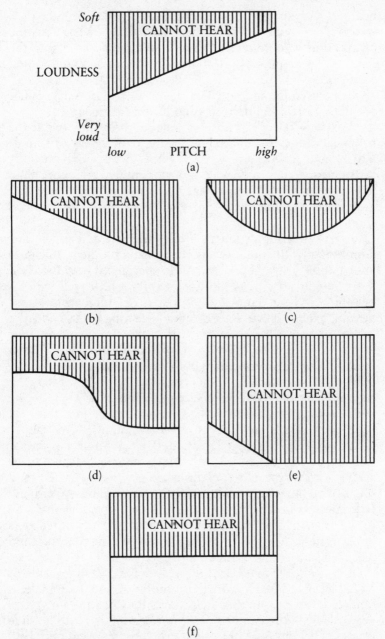

Note: Axes of diagrams as in (a)

Figure 3.2 The different shapes of hearing difficulties

hearing and be worse off with high-pitched sounds than low-pitched sounds. Once again, if we draw lines across the diagram they would rarely be flat and horizontal – that is, the same across all pitches. More usually they take many shapes. Figure 3.2 contains some examples of possible shapes. Look at them carefully and compare them with Figure 3.1. What are the different children missing around their world?

Thus children may not be able to hear the telephone ringing, but they may be able to hear a baby crying or sounds like *m* and *n*. Are they 'playing-up' to be more partially hearing than they are? This is a possibility, but more than likely the shape of their hearing impairment is such that high-pitched sounds are more affected than low-pitched sounds.

How do hearing problems affect language and education? Simplistically, the more severe the hearing problem, the more affected the language and the more specialised help the child needs in education. The child who cannot hear well will not be able to hear language properly. Children who have hearing problems will have trouble detecting the sounds that make up words, which in turn make up language. For example, let's take Peter's hearing problem. Peter has a moderate hearing problem in both ears. Although he can hear the vowel sounds and some consonants of low pitch, he cannot hear the high-pitched consonants *f*, *th*, *s*, nor the medium-pitched consonants *ch*, *sh*, *k* and *g*. Just think of how many words are made up of these sounds. Peter cannot detect all that is said to him, and as a result he cannot understand language well. It is important for teachers to be aware of the intimate relationship between hearing and speech and language. Children with questionable speech and language should always have their hearing tested, as this may be where their problem lies. It is the responsibility of teachers to refer these children for testing, thus ensuring that the child will receive the appropriate help.

Many children who are found to have hearing problems wear hearing aids. Hearing aids amplify sound, they make it louder, so effectively they help the child's hearing line move upwards, so more can be heard. But hearing aids are not like glasses. They do not correct the problem, they can only help make it less severe. The crucial difference is that for the ear, louder does not mean clearer. The hearing aid makes sounds louder for the child, but as with a loudspeaker addressing a crowd, what is said is not necessarily more intelligible. The hearing aid is thus just the first step in helping the child. These children still need specialised help with their language and school work. For example, hearing-impaired children will need to sit at the front of the class, with their best ear pointing towards the teacher, so that they can take maximum advantage of the incoming visual information (e.g. lip-reading) as well as their residual hearing. They will also benefit from having oral instructions confirmed in writing and from general help in developing their oral language, writing and reading skills.

But not all hearing losses are permanent and incurable. The presence of middle ear problems such as 'glue ear' can produce a hearing loss. This type of loss related to middle ear dysfunction is termed a *conductive* loss, in contrast to 'nerve' or *sensori-neural* losses we have so far talked about. Conductive hearing losses are common in children. It usually manifests itself as a flat loss across all pitches (see (f) in Fig. 3.2) which varies across time depending on the condition of the middle ear. If the child has a cold, he may have fluid in his ear and thus a hearing loss, but once the cold clears, the loss disappears only to return again once he starts getting a stuffy nose! Children can have pure conductive losses, but also they can have a mixture of sensori-neural losses, topped up with conductive losses. This is very confusing to teachers and professionals working with hearing-impaired children, as it is difficult to know just how bad their hearing is. On a good day, when their middle ear is clear, they perform well, while another day they seem to be 'naughty' and not listening at all. Beware, as it may be that their middle ear is not working properly and their hearing loss is actually worse on that day. The best help for children with conductive loss is to refer them for medical help so that the cause of the conductive loss can be treated and the middle ear cleared.

Brain and language

In this section we want to suggest that although language remediation is not going to involve direct physical action on the brain, there are some pointers to language remediation processes which are supported by our knowledge of how a child's brain functions and develops. Knowing about how the brain is organised can give us clues as to why some remedial approaches are successful and not others.

We are not born with fully developed brains; the brain is growing throughout childhood, but this growth is not a steady expansion. There are periods of development followed by periods of relatively little change, and these brain growth spurts continue into the teenage years.

It has been suggested, not unreasonably, that unevenness of a child's intellectual development is closely associated with the uneven pattern of brain growth. This may well be right but should be treated with caution as it is not yet clear whether spurts in intellectual development happen at the same time as brain growth; or whether the periods of brain growth provide the necessary foundation for the mental development which follows later. In other words, does brain development precede or accompany the growth of the mind? Whatever the correct answer to this question, the prediction is still that at some points children will develop more rapidly than others. This would be borne out by any experienced teacher who will tell you that children often make rapid progress after some time at an educational plateau. They suddenly seem to understand topics which had for months or even years seemed beyond them.

People often interpret attempts to involve the brain in our understanding of education as reducing education to biology. These criticisms often imply that to talk about the brain in an educational context is to assume physical limits on what any child can be taught; in other words, if a child does not learn something easily, it is because he is limited by the brain. This view is a serious misunderstanding. The real educational message from the study of brain development is that we should keep trying to teach children despite their learning difficulties because if some additional brain maturation is required for learning, then this growth may well be on its way.

Although we must be very cautious about assuming *causal* relationships between intellectual milestones and brain maturation, the evidence of Epstein is that there are five major periods of brain growth between 3 to 10 months, 2 to 4 years, 6 to 8 years, 10 to 12 years and 14 to 16 years. And it is certainly striking how these periods overlap with the well-known developmental stages of Piaget.

Language, like other higher mental processes, requires integrating separate sub-components which have their primary location in separate parts of the brain. And language itself expresses information which is processed by other regions. Sometimes this information results from perception of objects and events that are visually present, or alternatively, long-term memory might be required. Often both present and past events are compared in one linguistic expression involving visual perception and memory as well as the language areas. The integration of these and other brain functions such as selective attention and arousal reveal successful language processing as involving the integration and sequencing of the activities of many parts of the brain.

As will be seen from the case histories discussed in this book, most language disorders cannot be identified with the failure to function of one, or even two, specific parts of the brain. Many of these children have difficulties at the level of integration and organisation of information which calls on a number of different brain functions (see, for example, David in Ch. 6, p.59). We have a long way to go before the control processes for these complex activities can be identified with the brain's physiology or biochemistry. But the parallel between our understanding of language behaviour and the brains's activities is good in as far as both involve complex interrelationships between sub-components. And the key to understanding both language and the brain lies in the organisational principles between, for example, intonation and word selection or right and left hemisphere.

We do know that some aspects of the physical nature of the brain's growth can be directly influenced by the child's environment. The nerve cells or neurons of the brain make many interconnections with each other. And the amount of contact between nerve cells has been shown to relate to environmental factors ranging from the amount and type of sensory stimulation, to the child's diet. Malnutrition is all too prevalent a cause of retarded brain development.

The brain has many different parts which appear to have

different functions. These parts are interlinked by nerve cells whose function seems to be to keep one part of the brain in communication with another. In general the larger linking cell fibres seem to be well formed at birth, with their interconnections well established, while the local area nerve cells develop during infancy and depend on sensory stimulation for their development and maintenance. Hence environmental influences like malnutrition and sensory deprivation are more likely to influence those local area networks with specific functions rather than the long interconnecting fibres. But genetic abnormalities and damage by injury or disease may equally harm both types of neurons.

With respect to language processing, there are three main areas involved. Broca's area, Wernicke's area and the angular gyrus. And these three are strongly interconnected by bundles of nerve fibres (Fig. 3.3). Broca's area is closely involved in the formulation of language sequencing. As a consequence, damage to this area can lead to misarticulation of speech sounds, ungrammatical utterances and various types of spelling problems. The resulting speech will have short phrase lengths with relatively few function words. Comprehension of language can often be largely unaffected.

Damage to Wernicke's area, in contrast, produces very poor language comprehension, and while speech is grammatical it reveals deficiencies in content words (i.e. nouns and verbs). Repetition of other peoples' speech is often problematic for both Broca's and Wernicke's 'aphasics'. Both Broca's and Wernicke's areas are situated in the left hemisphere of the brain, and damage to the right hemisphere does not produce severe language problems in right-handed people, although problems with the intonation of speech may be found. The angular gyrus has the function of integrating auditory and visual information, consequently it plays an important role in reading and writing. When a written word is read aloud the information goes initially to the angular gyrus via the visual cortex. From the angular gyrus the integrated visual and auditory information goes to Wernicke's area, where its significance is assessed. It then passes on to Broca's area and then to the parts of the motor cortex which control the mechanisms of articulation. It should perhaps be stressed that this account of the localisation of

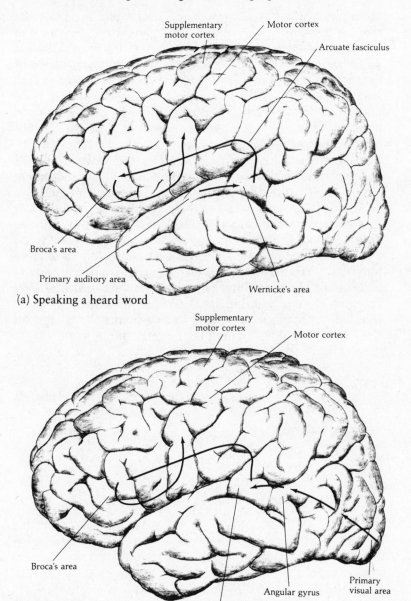

(a) Speaking a heard word

(b) Speaking a written word

Figure 3.3 Brain areas involved in language processing (source: Richard F. Thompson, *The Brain*, 1985)

brain function is based on the developed brain. It is less clear that the developing system has this degree of specificities, and some neurologists would even be inclined to argue that the adult brain does not have quite the degree of localisation of function just outlined. However, the essential point is that language processing involves communication between different parts of the brain in an integrated and organised way. Breakdown in the integration processes can produce problems as well as damage to the areas involved.

In summary, then, current views of the way our brains develop and function suggest a wide range of subtly different language difficulties rather than a few very similar problems. Also, it is likely that with age these problems may change or disappear, sometimes to reappear later. Most important of all, it is thought that language remediation may need to be extended over quite long periods of time for any one child and may require a very wide ranging approach, taking account of skills as different as story-telling and synonym recognition, and bearing in mind that it is the successful integration of these activities which makes language so flexible as a tool of communication and thought.

4

Working with
Language Disabilities

Language is the most powerful social tool a human being can have. Language tells us what a person thinks, feels and wants, it allows us to share and communicate with other people, and it enables us to bring about change and make events happen. Children with language disabilities face the frustration of not being able to use language easily; for these children language is a difficult and demanding task. In order to overcome their problems these children need more than the dedication and care of their teachers. They need to participate in a carefully thought-out teaching plan, designed to help their particular individual language difficulties.

SCORE: a model for language teaching

Teachers are usually confronted with the awesome task of discriminating and choosing among the many available language programmes and/or having to develop their own teaching plan to fit the children's communicative needs. How can we go about carrying out these tasks? What factors must be taken into account?

The SCORE model is an attempt to answer these questions. It describes five essential principles involved in language teaching. The model is not revolutionary by any means. It is based on common sense, research and experience, and it recognises the fact that teachers inevitably have the greatest responsibility for children's learning. Other professionals may be involved, and indeed may offer help and advice, but at the end of the day it is the teacher who spends a great deal of time with the child, it is the teacher who knows the child best and, most important of all, it is the teacher that can help. Successful teaching will need to take into account the five basic principles:

> The Situation in which language is taught
> The Contrasts between different aspects of language
> The Order in which the child is taught
> The Regularity of our communications with the child
> The Encouragement we give the child as we teach.

We will now examine these principles in more detail before going on to look at them in action with particular children.

Situation

The more natural the teaching situation, the more likely it is that the child will encounter a similar situation in his everyday activities. Natural communication is reinforcing as it allows one to get what one wants, express one's feelings and opinions, develop relationships, and so on. If we can build our remedial programmes into natural communicative situations we greatly increase the motivation of the child to practice what he has been taught. We must avoid at all costs the temptation to set up a new and separate communicative context which the child only experiences during a language remediation programme.

Let us consider an example of poor teaching and suggest how to improve it by taking into account the situation principle. The objective is to teach the child to use the carrier phrase 'It's a . . . .' when talking about picture objects. The teaching session takes the following form. The teacher presents a picture of an object to the child and says, 'What's this?' The child responds, 'A clock'. The teacher says, 'No, it's a clock', and then provides the child with the imitative model, by saying, 'Say, it's a clock'. The child then imitates the model, the teacher smiles and says, 'Good'. The same procedure is followed for a set of ten pictures. The teacher drops the imitative model as soon as the child begins to respond consistently. By the end of the third session the child is using the carrier phrase 'It's a . . . .' consistently and without fail when talking about the pictures.

What is wrong? First, let's look at what is said. The teacher asks a question ('What is this?') to which the child needs to respond verbally. The child responds by saying, 'A clock', which is perfectly adequate by adult standards but unfortunately does not fit the established training goal. So what happens? The child is trained to ignore the adult form and instead is taught in a robot-like manner that to answer completely is to answer correctly. In many ways we have made the task of language learning more difficult for the child as he will be receiving conflicting imput at home and elsewhere. The child has had to separate language for communication (the language used at home or with friends to share ideas) and language as an exercise which one has to carry out in a specific way in an unnatural situation in which the teacher leads the interaction, knows what a clock looks like and what it is called, but still demands that the child tells what it is.

How can this activity be improved? In normal conversation we use the phrase 'It's a . . . .' when differentiating among objects using the negative. For example:

Mary: (*Looking at a new item in Sarah's kitchen.*) Sarah, is this a
          coffee pot?

Sarah: No, it's a teapot.

This example reminds us that a question derives its force from the fact that the person posing the question is not familiar with the answer. Thus, if one wants to provide a natural context in which the child can learn how to answer questions, the person asking the questions should not know the answer. The carrier phrase 'It's a . . . .' can then be used in a way which is appropriate to its natural usage.

In practice this might be done by playing a game with the child in which the child picks up a card but does not show it to the teacher. The teacher then guesses and if she is wrong, then the child tells her what the picture object is. The teacher will ask the child, 'Is it a clock?' and the child can answer positively ('Yes') or negatively ('No, it's a table').

Contrast

Therapeutic teaching of language occurs bit by bit, step by step. Usually, the child is taught a small portion of the linguistic system, and only after success with that portion does the child move on. Therefore, in many ways teaching language to a child is like giving the child pieces of a puzzle and hoping that he will put them together to form the entire picture. The principle of contrast helps the child to build this puzzle.

Teaching language using contrasts allows the teacher to provide the child with a framework within which the pieces of the puzzle can fit. Language is a system of contrasts, and the use of contrast in language teaching underlines the importance of relationships between different aspects of language; relationships between sounds, (e.g. tick and kick), relationships between words (e.g. banana – fruit) or relationship between utterances (e.g. The dog bit the cat – The cat was bitten by the dog.)

For example, when children are trying to learn the past tense it is important that they realise, among other things, how it is related to the present tense. By contrasting past actions with present actions the child is able to see the relationship between the two. Information presented in contrast allows children to relate new information to old information. Information presented in contrast also allows children to focus on a particular aspect of language. In the case of verb tenses, children will not be thinking about doing the action quickly, slowly or carefully, but how this action was done in the past and how it is done in the present. In this way, linguistic information presented in contrast helps children observe specific regularities in the language and thus begin to construct linguistic rules.

Now let's turn to two specific teaching problems: one the teaching of vocabulary items, and the other the teaching of sounds for appropriate pronunciation. In the first the aim of a teacher might be to teach the meaning of three verbs of locomotion (drive, sail and fly), using appropriate toys (a boat, a car, a plane, a little man, etc.), with the teacher producing appropriate utterances. Contrastive information involves pointing out similarities – 'We can travel on a boat,

a car or a plane'; 'We can sail/fly/drive quickly or slowly' –
and differences – 'Can you fly a boat? Can you fly a car? Can
you sail a plane?' Further contrasts would indicate that each
action takes place in a different medium. 'The aeroplane flies
in the air – can the boat sail in the air? The man drives the car
on the road – can the car go in the water?' This contrastive
information begins to specify the meaning of the words in
question with the minimum of ambiguity.

The second problem is a familiar one to many teachers.
Children who have difficulty developing the sound system of
their language have problems being understood because they
use sounds unsystematically. Take for example the child who
does not differentiate between *t* and *k*; that is, the child uses *t*
for both *t* and *k* and thus fails to differentiate between words
such as:

*t*ick – *k*ick
tea – *k*ey
*t*ap – *c*ap

An approach to remediation which did not use the contrast
principle might require the child to practice simple words
such as 'key', 'koo', 'kay' and then gradually introduce more
complex words into therapy. But the child has not been
presented with anything to contrast with *k*. Instead, the
sound has been learned in isolation from the other sounds in
the system. Using the contrast principle, the teacher contrasts
the target sound *k* with the *t* sound that the child is using in
its place. The child's attention is focused on the contrast that
he is failing to make by pairing words which are identical
except for one key sound. Following are examples of these
minimal pairs:

initial t – k	*initial p – b*	*final m – n*
*t*ick – *k*ick	*p*ig – *b*ig	ti*n* – Ti*m*
tea – *k*ey	*p*ea – *b*ee	pa*n* – Pa*m*

Minimal pairs are selected which represent concrete objects
so that the teacher can draw them and the child can identify
them easily. First, the child is taught to discriminate between
the two sounds; that is, to hear the difference between the
two sounds. For this purpose the teacher presents the child
with a pair of pictures (tea – key), says one of the words (tea),

and the child has to point to the correct picture. Then the child becomes the leader, and the teacher has to do the pointing and will make deliberate mistakes to see if the child recognises them as such. The child is also encouraged to learn to group the sounds that go together. Two columns are made, one headed 'T' and the other headed 'K'. The child is then asked to put the picture under the correct column. The teacher says the word, the child finds the picture and then has to put it under the correct column.

Second, the child is taught to say the words containing the sound contrast. For this purpose the teacher repeats the above procedure but instead of saying one of the words of the pair, he simply points to one, and the child has to say what it is. During the child's attempts to pronounce the sounds, the teacher helps the child by explaining what he has to do. For example, when trying to produce *k* the teacher mentions the fact that it has to come all the way from the back of the throat.

Order

The order in which language sounds, structures and concepts are taught is important because language is a complex, interrelated system and thus needs to be built systematically. All plans for teaching language make choices about order, but these choices are not always made sensibly. Decisions about order are often made in ways that fail to take the child's perspective into account. For example, the 'fill the gap' approach to teaching language looks for gaps in the child's system and tries to fill them. This approach relies on the teacher's intuitions about what the child should know. Unfortunately, there may be a mismatch between what the child is being taught and what he is ready to learn.

There are two main ordering principles which have proven to be effective. First there is the functional approach, which is often appropriate with children of limited ability. The assumption made is that these children will not be able to learn the language system fully and thus need to learn those aspects of language which will enable them to effectively communicate their needs and desires. The order of language teaching in this case is based on providing the child with structures and concepts that will prove useful, e.g. food, dress, toilet, requests and refusals. The precise set of structures and concepts to be taught to the child will be closely linked to the type of environment the child is in. For example, the child who is living at home will probably be taught different aspects of language from the child who is living in a sheltered environment such as a community hospital.

The second ordering principle is based on the developmental approach. This principle suggests that we teach language to the language-disabled child in the same order that normal language-learning children acquire language. To do this, the teacher has to become thoroughly familiar with the existing language system of the language-disabled child so that it can be compared to that of a normal language-learning child.

Let's take as an example teaching the child how to use the words 'front' and 'back' appropriately. Studies of normal language development have shown that children initially understand the meaning of 'front' and 'back' with reference to themselves (the child's own back and front). Then they master the usage of these words when referring to objects with clear fronts (a teddy bear's front, a cooker's back, a telephone's front), and finally usage with reference to non-fronted objects is learned (in front of or at the back of a glass, a brick, a ball). This order of the normal developmental process suggests a sequence of contexts in which we might lead the child to a full understanding of 'front' and 'back' – a sequence which may well make use of a natural order of difficulty. In addition to careful consideration of functional and development principles of orders, we may often in practice have to make decisions of sequence which are based on individual children's learning preferences. Children frequently show capacity to learn aspects of particular experiences. Good teaching is always capable of modifying general principles to fit individual children.

Regularity

The regularity principles of therapeutic teaching involves organising the language input to the child in a consistent manner. A child's language environment involves the teachers, parents and many others, and all these people should regulate the way they talk to the child. Currently, it is all too common to find, for example, a child who has intensive therapy on the contrasts between *t* and *k* once a week but for the rest of the time gets no specific help. As in this case, language-disabled children often receive irregular doses of remedial input, and the task of language learning will consequently take longer.

Regularity is also very important within the teaching situation itself, but can be very difficult to sustain. For example, consider a child learning to use the auxiliary 'is' by describing what he sees in photographs of members of his family doing various activities (daddy is sleeping, mummy is reading). Sometimes the child omits the auxiliary but talks particularly clearly. At other times, the child includes 'is' correctly but speaks unclearly. Giving the child a sense of knowing *when* and *why* he is doing well will require great care and very skilful explanation by the teacher. Regularity in language teaching must be such that the children understand which aspects of their language the teacher is praising or correcting.

Encouragement
We must not lose sight of the human, emotive component when designing a teaching plan. Concern with the situation, the contrasting process, the order and regularity of language teaching, may force us to think along abstract, technical lines. This is why we have included encouragement as the final principle in our language-teaching model. Encouragement in language teaching is not only revealed in the way the teacher interacts and teaches the child but in the way he plans for the child, listens to the child, accepts the child. Encouragement is a strong force in the language-teaching/learning process: it demonstrates to the child that the steps he is going through are worth taking.

What we have done so far is simply explain briefly what the elements of the SCORE model are. We have yet to see the model in action, see how teachers may use these principles to help language-disabled children in their schools.

5

Phonological Disabilities

How do we produce speech sounds?

At the turn of the century, William A. Spooner, Dean of New College, Oxford, became well known not for his academic achievements but because of his way of speaking. His tendency to reverse both sounds and words — as in 'You've *hi*ssed my *my*stery lectures' or '*Work* is the curse of the *drinking* classes' — became known as 'Spoonerisms'. Spooner did not rehearse these errors in order to be funny, but he produced them spontaneously in speech. These errors provide us with a clue as to how we organise our speech. It is obvious from the evidence of Spoonerism that we do not plan our speech one word at a time. Instead, we preplan what we are going to say and anticipate the words to come. When Spooner said 'hissed' instead of 'missed' he was thinking of the word 'history' that was coming later, and this interfered with speech production.

We are used to seeing words separated in written text but we do not speak one word at a time. Speech is a continuous stream, one word blending into the next with some pauses taken for breath. Talking is a highly skilled activity where complex movements involved in our oral musculature are smoothly sequenced to produce speech.

The influence of written text also results in another misconception. Because we learn twenty-six letters of the alphabet and we spell all English words with these letters, it is often thought that children need to learn twenty-six sounds in order to speak; but in fact, for English, there are approximately forty such sounds (phonemes). Just compare these two words:

gem   game

The g for gem is a different sound (phoneme) from the g for game, although they are both represented by the letter g. This can also be seen in the phonemes involved in 'thin – clothes', 'measure – sunset' and many more. The forty phonemes of English are very different from each other. Some are produced at the back of the mouth (k,g) others are produced in the middle (t, n) while others are produced in the front (p, b).

Air is the power supply for speech. Just try to speak while you hold your breath and you will realise that no sounds will be produced. When we speak, air comes from the lungs and it works its way up through our larynx where it finds the vocal folds. Two things can happen here. First, we can make the air pressure vibrate the vocal folds, which results in 'voicing' (like saying 'ah'), or we can let the air pass through the vocal folds into the mouth, where depending on how we move our tongue, lips, and so on, it results in different sounds without voicing (like th, s). These different movements of our tongue, soft palate, lips are sequenced and co-ordinated in speech planning, which directs motor impulses to our muscles (to contract or relax) so that we can lift our tongue for t or close our soft palate for k or our lips for p. Producing speech sounds is therefore a complex task, involving the brain, musculature, oral mechanisms and respiratory systems. It is not surprising, then, that we find children who have difficulties producing the phonemes (speech sounds) of English. Many things can go wrong in the process of producing properly sequenced sounds, and it is to these difficulties that we now turn.

Phonological disabilities: recognisable physical causes

Children with dysarthria
Children with dysarthria have problems producing the standard speech sounds (phonemes) of their language or dialect because of abnormalities in the structure involved in

speech production such as the lips, teeth, tongue, palate, and so on, or neuromuscular abnormalities which result in difficulty controlling and co-ordinating the movements necessary to produce phonemes. Children with cerebral palsy or paralysis secondary to head injury often have dysarthric speech. Dysarthric children produce partly or wholly unintelligible speech, and they need intensive help to achieve a functional level of intelligibility.

Given the different structures involved in speech production and the damage that can occur to them, dysarthria covers a wide range of children, from those with very mild difficulties, such as lack of soft-palate control in order to produce *k* and *g*, to those children who are severely floppy, cannot walk, have difficulties in controlling breathing and who possibly will not ever be able to communicate using speech. Depending on the school in which they work, teachers may well encounter children throughout this range.

When paying attention to even mild speech difficulties in children it is important to remember that they may have a physical base such as poor control of the soft palate or a weakness of the oral muscles. It can be helpful to remember that we do more than just speak with our mouths: we eat, we drink, we blow, we whistle. If there is a problem in the oral structure, it should affect all the mouth's activities. Thus a child who has difficulty pronouncing some of his consonants clearly, who also sometimes drools a little bit, who takes longer than everyone else to finish eating, is the sort of child who is easily missed because he is not too bad. But it is this type of child who needs exercises which strengthen his muscles and help him overcome his difficulties.

The following is a case example of Mary, a dysarthric girl. Her case illustrates some of the points discussed above. Mary is a 10-year-old girl who attends a language unit but will be moving to a residential language school because of severe problems with producing speech sounds. Mary had a normal birth history, which gives no indication as to the reason for her physical disability. Mary has a mild right hemiparesis (the right side of her body cannot be moved as fully as her left) as well as severe dysarthria. She has poor movement of the vocal mechanism to articulate sounds, some loss of sensation in the tongue and general poor motor co-ordination. Her tongue, lips and mouth are not well co-ordinated for making different sounds. These physical problems have in no way affected Mary's general intellectual abilities or her ability to understand language. Indeed, Mary performs well within the normal range in these areas. She is an active, independent girl who can cope with all activities necessary for daily living.

Mary's speech is completely unintelligible to strangers. Given her limited tongue and lip movement, her speech has an unclear quality to it. To get a feeling for what Mary's speech sounds like, put one finger in your mouth, underneath your tongue and speak. The following interaction with her language unit teacher shows her reading sentences and not spontaneous dialogue; it illustrates the difficulty her speech presents to those trying to understand what she says:

(1) Teacher: Let's try some of the sentences that you may have to say when you are at home. Let's try this one *(pointing to a card)*.

(2) Mary: I watsh sho so shoe shle shop. *[I want to go to the shop.]*

(3) Teacher: That was nice the 'p' at the end of 'shop'.

(4) Mary: I wantsh my pchle pshlesh mum. [I want my tea please mum.]

(5) Teacher: That 'mum' was very clear, wasn't it Mary? You can do your 'm's.

This sort of articulatory disability requires around the clock, mouth and tongue exercises such as lip-rounding, pursing lips as if for kissing, moving the tongue upwards, downwards and sideways, and so on, as well as practice on each sound to make them slowly clearer and clearer. In many ways therapy consists of fighting with Mary's physical difficulties. These difficulties also affect other functions of the oral mechanism, such as swallowing, controlling saliva and chewing. The therapeutic process involved in cases like Mary's will be lengthy and arduous given the severity of her difficulties. Mary, though well motivated, might well be encouraged to use writing for communication, whenever this could be reasonably socially appropriate. Mary is at present in a residential school for children with language problems and receives daily intensive therapy from her teacher as well as speech therapists.

Dysarthria can affect children's social life with their peers, but much of this depends on the severity of the problem as well as the personality of the child. The following *story* about Neil illustrates this point rather well.

Neil is a 5-year-old boy with mild cerebral palsy and accompanying dysarthria. Neil's speech is rather difficult to understand, and because of his cerebral palsy he tends to fall down more than his peers. Neil receives physiotherapy and speech therapy at his local school and is described by those who know him as a ray of sunshine. He chatters away and quickly tries to get up when he falls. He has lots of friends around his home and co-operates with his teacher and all his therapists.

Neil's mother was told by his teacher and speech therapist what cerebral palsy was and how it affected his speech. Neil was in the room at the time, but the teacher and the therapist were not aware of how much he was taking in. When he came home after school, he ran outside to see his friends and was heard to say the following:

Neil: Hey, Hey! I know why I talk funny.

A friend: Why Neil?

Neil: I have *terrible palsy*.

Another friend: And how does it feel Neil?

Neil: Terrible!

Children with dyspraxia
Dyspraxic children have great difficulty producing the standard speech sounds of their language or dialect but, unlike dysarthic children, have no obvious general physical problems (paralysis or structural abnormalities of the lips, tongue, etc.) However, they do have difficulties in programming the patterns of movements required for speech. Recall our discussion on speech production and the importance of organising and sequencing the complex movements involved

in running speech. Dyspraxic children have problems in preplanning as well as in motor planning, which are activities organised by the central nervous system. It is not surprising then that dyspraxic children often show general motor co-ordination problems.

In the experience of most teachers, there is at least one case of the 'clumsy' child. That child is usually not bad enough to be classified as motorically impaired, but he is usually that bit worse off than his peers when it comes to motor planning and co-ordination. Speech, we have seen, is a highly skilled motor activity, and as such it may not work smoothly for such clumsy children. The problems can be very mild. The child may have difficulty with words which have three or more syllables, such as elephant, rhinocerous, pineapple, where planning and sequencing are important; and he may have difficulty imitating what the teacher has said because this requires focusing on the teacher's words and co-ordinating his own speech mechanisms to repeat what was said. Just as these children need to practice general motor co-ordination activities, they also need practice with their speech, no matter how mild the problem appears to be at first sight. These children need that extra 'time on task' so that the task of sequencing sounds to form words becomes easier for them. They need activities where words which have been identified as difficult for the child are used repeatedly. The child then has the chance to rehearse the motor patterns of difficult words enough to consolidate them and for the whole sequencing and planning aspects of the experience to become unconscious. On the other hand, these activities need to be fun, relevant and communicative for the child. We must try to follow the situation principle from the SCORE model, trying to create a natural teaching situation. A useful guide to this is to take the child's own spontaneous language and use it to make up stories and games containing the difficult target words.

Following is the case example of Robin, a dyspraxic child. Robin is a 9-year-old child attending a language unit. His birth history was uneventful and he began to develop normally but at 4 years of age, Robin had acquired only a handful of unintelligible words for communication. He started speech therapy then but developed severe middle ear problems that year, which affected his speech therapy attendance and his progress. This problem was finally treated by inserting grommets in both his ears for drainage of the fluid behind his eardrums. At this time it also became apparent that Robin was rather clumsy and that he exhibited moderate learning difficulties. Despite the presence of these difficulties, it was thought that Robin's speech problems were not directly related to his learning problems but instead were specific to his difficulties in imitating mouth movements and reproducing the sound patterns of words. These difficulties were not due to paralysis or structural abnormality, as Robin's swallowing and chewing patterns were perfectly normal, but were due to a central nervous system problem. In other words, Robin showed the characteristics of a dyspraxic child; that is, he had tremendous difficulties sequencing simple sounds to make words *in the absence* of paralysis or physiological abnormalities of the vocal mechanism.

Below is a portion of dialogue between Robin and his teacher. Teacher and child are playing with a variety of toys on the floor of a quiet room.

(1) Teacher: So what are you doing?
(2) Robin: Make tea.
(3) Teacher: Make tea, right. I'd like a cup of tea please.
(4) Robin: Milk and ugar? [Milk and sugar?]
(5) Teacher: Not for me, thank you. Would you?
(6) Robin: No.
(7) Teacher: Tell me, how did you make the tea?
(8) Robin: Et om water. [Get some water.]
(9) Teacher: Um-hum.
(10) Robin: U i rai there *(pointing to the kettle)*. [Put it right there.]

From this portion of dialogue it is evident that Robin's speech is still far from normal. He has great difficulty imitating simple sounds such as *s, p, t,* but it helps him a lot if he can see the sound written down and/or a picture of the object he has to name.

Thus, over the last year, the language unit teacher and speech therapist have tried to use reading as the means to help Robin monitor his speech. The idea is to have Robin learn to sight read very simple monosyllabic words which contain simple consonants (m, t, d, k, f) but not blends (st, kr, scr) such as 'mat', 'bin', 'nut', 'net', 'bag', 'fan', and so on. This set of monosyllabic words form his core sight-reading vocabulary, and it is used to make simple sentences for Robin to read. Some examples are:

> The dog is on the mat.
> The cap is on the doll.
> The man is on the bus.

The sentences are used accompanied by pictures. The aim is to have Robin practice these words so much that they begin to be produced automatically without him being conscious of the sequences of sounds involved in the words. This rehearsal is aimed at facilitating his motor planning. Slowly, more words are added to the core vocabulary and the complexity of the words is increased.

It is thought that reading can help Robin's oral language because reading provides Robin with the opportunity to have words presented to him *simultaneously* for scanning and review. Oral language is always *sequential*, and thus it has special demands on auditory memory and temporal processing. When speaking, Robin has to listen, monitoring his own speech. When uttering a sentence, he must retain what he has said while completing a thought. In contrast, reading or written language is not sequential and is more permanent. Robin can use written language as a device to help him learn and remember the sequences of sounds words are made of and to monitor his speech. Also, seeing words written down often helps Robin to understand how the words are segmented into different sounds. Of course, this is not always easy in English as there is not a one-to-one correspondence between how a word is spelt and how it is pronounced, but his teacher is aware of this and she chooses words such as 'mat', 'bin', and 'nut', where there is such a correspondence.

The preparation of material to help dyspraxic children is a very time-consuming activity. However, the Nuffield Speech and Hearing Centre (Royal National Throat, Nose and Ear Hospital, Swinton Street, London) can make available their Dyspraxic Programme with over 400 sheets of materials.

Phonological disabilities non-recognisable physical causes

Children with phonological disabilities
This type of child is puzzling because despite adequate motor planning and apparently intact neurophysiology, they have difficulties communicating because of unintelligible speech. These children have no apparent difficulties producing speech sounds, but it is as if they have either mislearned or have not yet learned when it is appropriate to use sound contrasts to form words. They do not seem to have apprehended the rules which tell us how sounds are organised in speech. So, for example, a particular child may always use a *k* sound where a *t* sound should be used. Because the system of rules which govern the use of sounds (phonemes) is called the phonological system, these children are referred to as having phonological disabilities. Unfortunately, our knowledge of the possible causes of this problem is very limited, and at present there is little agreement among researchers in this area. Also, it is often difficult in practice to differentiate between dyspraxic children and phonologically disabled children. Both groups of children have no obvious general physical problems, but they present with unintelligible speech. In theory, dyspraxic children have motor-planning difficulties while phonologically disabled children do not. But motor planning is something which is quite difficult to test. Once again we want to emphasise that children do not fall neatly into discrete categories of disability, and thus labelling a child dyspraxic or phonologically disabled is not in itself going to help. What we need to be aware of is the different areas of possible difficulty with language and try to apply them to the individual child in question.

One possible hint as to the nature of the problem comes from the fact that phonological difficulties (difficulties with the use of sounds) seem to come hand in hand with grammatical disabilities (difficulties with putting words together to form utterance). It is indeed rare to find a child who has severe phonological difficulties but has no problem producing age-appropriate grammar. These children differ in the degree to which their phonology and grammar are impaired. Some children have mild phonological problems but severe grammatical problems. (They speak in very short, telegraph-like sentences, such as 'Adam sit car' or 'Me want truck'). Others have mild grammatical difficulties but severe phonological problems. It seems that there is an intimate relationship between the sound system (phonology) and the grammatical system (syntax). It may be that in many cases the cause of one of these problems is the cause of the other. Alternatively, the way in which a child tries to solve difficulties in one area might induce errors in the other. As would be predicted therefore, we shall encounter children with phonological disabilities in the next section on grammatical disabilities. In our view, while it is useful to make the distinction for purposes of analysis and exposition, when it comes to dealing with real children we must beware of seeing their problems as only phonological or grammatical. They usually come hand in hand.

It takes most average children approximately seven years to master the sound system of English. Thus, by the time the child enters junior school he should comfortably use all the sound contrasts needed for conversation. The process of learning, though, is a gradual one. Young children first learn the simple stop and nasal consonants (p, b, t, d, k, g, m, n) and *w*; then they learn the fricative sounds (f, v, th, s, z, sh) and glides (l, y), followed by the more difficult *ch*, *r* and the consonant clusters (br, gr, st, spr, etc.). The learning is characterised by certain simplifications. Children do not wait until they learn the fricative *s* before using words which begin with 's' like soap; instead, they tend to replace the fricative with a stop consonant and they may say 'doap'. Also young normal language learning children tend to pay attention to the beginning of words and they may delete final consonants. Now our word 'soap' which became 'doap' may now become 'dough' after the deletion of the final 'p'. They also tend to simplify the syllable structure of words and drop one syllable to make things easier, thus 'banana' becomes 'nana' and elephant becomes 'ephant'. All these normal processes gradually disappear as the child grows older. Many teachers, however, will encounter in their classrooms children whose language is immature. They are slow at getting rid of the aforementioned processes and thus their phonology is much like that of younger children. Also, teachers may encounter children who 'get stuck' on one problem, for example substituting *w* for *r* and calling rabbits 'wabbits'. The amount of help a child needs is based on the same principles as these outlined in the SCORE model. Lets now turn to the case example of Mark to illustrate this point. Mark's phonological difficulties are severe enough to make it difficult for unfamiliar people to understand what he is saying. Note, though, that the sentences Mark uses are short for a 4-year-old, illustrating the accompanying grammatical problems.

Mark is a 4-year-old child who attends nursery school and regular speech therapy at his local clinic. Mark was born one month prematurely, weighing 5 lbs 10 oz. No complications were present at birth. He was a bit of a slow developer and by 3 years of age he only expressed himself with single words and gestures. He had a history of earaches and frequent colds, but tests revealed Mark's hearing to be normal in both ears. Non-verbal abilities did not appear impaired either. Mark performed well within the normal range in formal tests. Parents felt Mark understood all that was said to him but could not talk 'properly'. Mark's mother understood what he said, less so his father, and his friends and strangers had difficulty understanding him. This worried Mark's parents and nursery teacher, and they reported that they felt he may not grow out of the habit of mispronouncing words.

Assessment of Mark's understanding of language confirmed the parental report that Mark understood language like other children his own age. He was able to follow complex instructions ('Put the red block under the chair'), understand weight differences (heavy–light), identify objects by their description ('Show me which one we cut with') and identify a variety of body parts (heel, elbow, little finger). Mark's speech, though, was difficult to understand, and his utterances were short and simple in grammatical structure. Below is a portion of dialogue between Mark and his nursery teacher. His nursery teacher has worked very hard at understanding Mark's speech, and has also worked closely with the speech therapist on Mark's language programme.

Teacher and child are in a corner of the classroom, playing with a garage and cars.

(1) Teacher: You are playing with the toys.
(2) Mark: Da my ta. [That my car.]
(3) Teacher: That is your car, yes.
(4) Mark: Da boten.
               [That broken.]
(5) Teacher: Oh, that *is* broken ...... the car is broken.
(6) Mark: I bod my ta.
               [I broke my car.]
(7) Teacher: Oh, dear.
               Don't worry, I think it was already broken.
               What are you going to do next?
(8) Mark: I ded ou.
               [I get out.]
(9) Teacher: Okay.

In this portion of dialogue it is evident that Mark is not using all the sound contrasts of English. He uses a lot of frontal sounds like *d* and *t* but not back sounds like *k* and *g*. He also drops some final consonants but includes others, although the latter are usually not correct (see Turns 6 and 8). Mark also simplified clusters like *br* and makes them into simple consonants like *b*. In addition, Mark often misses the auxiliary *is* and uses an average of two or three words together which results in very simple grammatical structures being used.

Mark receives language help concentrating on the development of his phonological (sound) system by doing activities involving minimal pairs of words such as "tea – key" (for his t – k problem), "game – dame" (for his g – d problem) as described in contrast principle in the SCORE model. Mark is also receiving help with his grammatical system by, among other activities, playing games with cards and objects involving the auxiliary *is* as described under the stiuation principle in the SCORE model. These activities are followed through by his nursery teacher at school and by his parents at home. Children who have milder cases of phonological difficulties still need help in constructing the pairs of sounds they have difficulty differentiating.

There is no doubt that impaired intelligibility of speech can have serious effects on the way the child interacts with his family and his peers. Not to be able to communicate one's needs and thoughts can be frustrating, as is illustrated in the following anecdote.

Daniel is a quiet 10-year-old, a Down's boy attending special school. When he speaks he does so with very short sentences. He often uses only two or three words together. Daniel does not like to answer questions much. He usually shrugs his shoulders and says 'Don't know' for an answer. But Daniel was not always like this. His class teacher comments that only a couple of years ago Daniel was a lively talker with a very outgoing personality. The trouble was that nobody could understand what Daniel was talking about!

Daniel had trouble with his sound contrasts: he could not tell his *t*'s from his *k*'s, could not put two sounds together to make blends like *tr*, *pl* or *sp*, neither could he control his voice to differentiate those sounds with voice (b, d, g) from those without (p, t, k). Two years ago, Daniel was unaware that people hardly understood his stories, his answers or his comments. When asked to repeat something he would do so willingly. But slowly Daniel began to realise that he could not be understood, and he became self-conscious and shy about his speech. Children with phonological difficulties need help from teachers, speech therapists and the family to avoid later social isolation and frustration.

6

Grammatical Disabilities: Organising Words into Language

In the English language the order in which words appear controls the meaning of what we say. The same words in different order may produce either sentences of a different meaning (e.g. 'John hit Bill', 'Bill hit John'), or it may produce strings of words with no meaning (e.g. 'John Bill hit'). Furthermore, adding or deleting words also changes meaning (e.g. 'John nearly hit Bill', 'John hit'). Additions and deletions may also produce meaningless utterances.

As shown in Chapter 2 on language development, normal children at the age of 2 are beginning to come to terms with the ways that word combinations influence meaning. This process of coming to understand the *grammar* of the language continues well into the school years as increasingly complex sentences are mastered. However there are many children in the language-disabled population for whom grammatical skills prove to be very problematic. This chapter discusses these children and examines the different reasons why their difficulties arise.

Before going on to describe individual children, there are two ways in which these children are often characterised which our experience suggests are neither accurate nor helpful. The first concerns the relationship between the comprehension and production of language; the second is about the relationship between phonological difficulties and grammatical difficulties, which are often seen as separate problems.

On the one hand, discussions of language-disabled children often make firm but unjustified diagnostic distinctions between problems in comprehension and production of speech. Labels like 'expressive aphasic' or 'receptive aphasic' are frequently written into case notes as an early substitute for understanding the full range of a child's difficulties. In this book we are trying to provide a framework for understanding the wide range of problems presented by the language-disabled population without suggesting that all these children fit neatly into a predetermined category. Assessment and diagnosis must involve classification but in a flexible and sensitive way that allows teachers to develop a richer description as the child provides more evidence of the way his problems interact with the language demands of different situations. Many children who have problems producing language also have accompanying communication problems. For example, a child who does not use pronouns in his speech (e.g. he, she, they, them) may well have trouble following instructions containing them. On the other hand, children whose problem centres around producing the right words and sentences (so that they do not say what they mean to say) are often referred to as having expressive language difficulties. These expressive problems are most commonly reflected in a delay in *both* the acquisition of the rules of the sound system of their native language or dialect (phonology) and also the ability to combine words together to produce age-appropriate sentences (grammar). These children are late in producing single words and in combining words to form sentences, and their speech is often unintelligible to a person who does not know them well. In this respect the child's sentences are very much like those of younger, normal language-learning children. It is indeed rare to find a child who has no phonological problems but has problems producing age-appropriate sentences or vice versa. For most of these children phonological difficulties and age-inappropriate grammar are the main features of the disorder, but the children differ in the degree to which their phonology and grammar are impaired. Some children have mild/

moderate phonological problems but severe grammatical problems. These are the children under focus in this section. Others have mild grammatical difficulties but severe phonological disorders (this group of phonological difficulties is described in Ch. 5, p. 45).

Practical experience tells us that phonological and grammatical problems interact with severity. The more severe the phonological problem, the more likely that the child will show grammatical difficulties in trying to put words together. Children's expressive problems will range from those with mild phonological disorders together with some expressive grammatical difficulties to those children who have severe difficulties producing both sounds and grammar. This range of children constitute the largest group of children with language disorders, and it contains more boys than girls, in the ratio of 3 : 1.

In general we can say that these young children with expressive problems will typically be:

a) Male.

b) Somewhere between 2 to 5 years of age at initial referral.

c) Case history: delayed onset of language.

d) Mother usually describes: I can understand him but nobody else can. He can understand everything you say.

e) Behaviour: somewhat erratic, hard to control, temper tantrums. The older the child, the more likely the presence of aggressive behaviour.

f) Hearing not impaired and does not have general learning difficulties.

Against this general background let us look at the case of Tim as an example of a child whose problems lie at the grammatical end of language production.

Tim is a 4-year-old attending regular speech therapy. Tim was born one month prematurely and was a breech birth. He then developed fairly normally: he sat at 6 months and walked at 18 months, but language was delayed. Tim did not produce single words until after two years of age, and he was delayed in putting two words together (after 3 years of age). Tim's parents did not worry too much about Tim because they felt he understood everything that was said to him and they just felt he was lazy about talking. They reported that Tim used a lot of gesture to accompany speech and in this way he could get his needs and desires understood. Tim was found to have normal hearing in both ears and to perform well within the normal range in non-verbal tests of ability. His comprehension of language was indeed what would be expected of a child his age: he recognised colours, he could pick objects by their description (show me the one that swims in the water), he could distinguish weight differences (heavy – light) and could follow instructions containing a variety of prepositions (in, on and under). The language he produced though was not easily understood, and the sentences he used were short and grammatically simple (an average of two to three words per sentence). Below is a portion of dialogue between Tim and his teacher. Teacher and child are playing with miniature farm toys on the floor of a quiet room.

(1) Teacher: What happened?
(2) Tim: Me do lie da *(showing teacher how he pushes a little toy boy around.)* [Me go like that.]
(3) Teacher: Oh!
(4) Tim: He do daddy, daddy ba. [He go daddy, daddy, back.]
(5) Teacher: Oh look! Where did he go? *(Teacher hides the little boy.)*
(6) Tim: Wa? [What?]
(7) Teacher: Where did he go?
(8) Tim: He de *(pointing to the toy boy).* [He there.]
(9) Teacher: He *is* there, yes.

It is evident from this portion of dialogue that Tim is a difficult child to understand. Tim's phonology – that is, his sound system – is like that of a much younger child. He drops all final consonants (that – da; what – wa) and he also does not use any back sounds like *k* or *g* but instead replaces them with more fronted sounds like *t* or *d* (go – do). His sentences are short and simple (see turns 2, 4, 6 and 8). In turn number 2, Tim uses 'me' instead of 'I', again something we would expect of a younger child but not a 4-year-old. In turn 8, Tim misses the verb 'is' and says 'He there' instead of 'He is there'. This is another example of his immature grammar.

Teaching is concentrating on developing Tim's sound system and grammar. Tim is exposed to sets of minimal pairs of words such as '*key*'/'*tea*', which contain the sounds that he is contrasting. The teaching activities and games follow closely the principles of situation and contrast described in the SCORE model as well as the other three principles. The teacher models more advanced sentences for Tim, an example of which is found in turns 8 and 9. Tim says 'He there', and the teacher repeats what he says but adds the verb by saying 'He *is* there'. Games and activities which require the use of different grammatical structures in appropriate situations are also part of Tim's teaching programme.

For example, play with toy people in familiar situations like a shop, farm or railway station can provide a context for varying the tense of verb forms – 'He was on the train', 'He is on the platform'. Dialogue between toy characters with one part being played by the child is also a useful way of focusing language on the child's needs.

An important recent technique for assessing children's grammatical problems is the Language Assessment and Remediation Screening Procedure (LARSP, Crystal, Fletcher and Garman, 1976). This takes a sample of a child's spoken language of about fifteen minutes duration. The grammatical structures used are counted, and a profile of use is produced as a standard form. The aim of teaching based on this assessment is to straighten the profile and eliminate imbalance in the child's grammar. It is a useful approach and is usable by teachers with little prior experience of linguistic assessments.

Understanding the way grammar works is crucial to our comprehension of language as well as its production. We are, of course, not consciously aware of grammatical rules in such a way that we could say what they are. But we are acutely aware when grammatical rules are not being followed because we cannot understand what we hear. Language-disabled children often have difficulties at this level of comprehension, and the next section discusses how these difficulties are revealed.

Problems using grammar to understand

As children grow older and begin to attend school, they continue to learn language. The school-aged child slowly develops an understanding of the small but critical units of language such as 'because', 'and', 'if', 'before', 'by'. He begins to use inference and thus gets better at 'reading between the lines'. He also learns how to handle sentences which do not follow the usual word order, such as 'the boy is kissed by the girl' and 'before you draw the picture, write a story'. But it is by no means always easy to know whether a child has full understanding of these aspects of language. It is very tempting to assume that if a child understands a certain word or sentence structure in a particular situation, he has complete mastery of that word or structure. Do children who understand 'because you're naughty' (as an explanation of a reprimand) understand all the uses of 'because' in the English language? The answer is No. Children use many clues to help them try to make sense of what they hear. They use knowledge of the world, familiarity, the situation and many other clues. Therefore we must be careful when drawing conclusions about children's abilities, because what may look like complete comprehension at first sight may not be full understanding due to mastery of language. Similarly, language-disabled children may appear to have understanding of language when in fact they still have problems, especially with the smaller units of language such as 'and', 'because' and 'before'. In order to help such children, we need to find out what children are really doing when they respond to language.

The two case examples which follow illustrate some of the ways language can appear to be understood by disabled children despite their problems. In many ways, these strategies and cues are the same as those used by normal language learners of a younger age, the difference being that the normal child will move on to more generally applicable ways of making sense of language without the help of teachers and therapists.

Geoffrey is a 12-year-old young man who attends an ordinary school and receives daily language help from a resource teacher. Amongst his language problems is a difficulty with passive structures (e.g. the chicken is chased by the duck). His teacher finds his comprehension variable: sometimes he seems to understand the passive structure and sometimes he does not. When Geoffrey is presented with an active sentence such as 'The chicken chases the duck' he uses a *typical-order* strategy to help his comprehension. This strategy assumes that the first noun–verb–noun sequence one hears reveals the relationship agent–action–recipient. Thus Geoffrey would follow the strategy: pick out the noun (chicken), verb (chase) and noun (duck) and assume it is the agent (chicken), action (chase) and recipient (duck). The result is: the CHICKEN CHASES the DUCK, which is the correct interpretation. But what happens when Geoffrey applies a similar strategy to sentences such as 'The chicken is chased by the duck?' Geoffrey applies the same strategy but now the result CHICKEN – CHASE – DUCK is the wrong interpretation. Indeed, this is exactly what happens to Geoffrey. He finds the passive structure very difficult and regularly misinterprets it. None the less, sometimes Geoffrey is able to get the right interpretation for passives. Why should this be? Is it because Geoffrey has mastery of the passive form and is just lazy, or is it because other factors influence comprehension? It turns out that Geoffrey can make use of his knowledge of the world to understand some passives. When Geoffrey is presented with sentences such as 'The grass is cut by the man' he applies the typical-order strategy and comes up with a GRASS – CUT – MAN interpretation. Geoffrey then uses his knowledge of the world as a cue and overrides his first interpretation. He knows the 'grass cannot cut men' so he is able to understand this passive sentence, which otherwise may have been too difficult for him. Thus, what may look like comprehension at first sight may be an application of real-world knowledge to a specific situation. *What* is said, *when* it is said and *how* it is said may help children like Geoffrey to understand. But there will obviously be limitations to the extent to which he can understand language in this way.

Another example of problems in understanding language is the case of Carol. Carol is a 9-year-old girl who attends a withdrawal language class in her local primary school. Carol has difficulties in understanding a variety of linguistic structures, including those which refer to events in time. As with Geoffrey, her performance is variable and her teacher often wonders if she indeed has a true difficulty with language comprehension. A close analysis of Carol's comprehension shows that she uses an *order-of-mention* strategy in order to understand sentences which express sequences of events and the relationship between them. If Carol is given a sentence like 'Move the boat before you move the car', she applies the order-or-mention strategy which leads her to move the items in the order she hears them. As a result she interprets the sentence as 'Move boat then car', which is the correct interpretation.

If we look at the analysis Carol has performed, we realise that she does not have to understand 'before' in order to interpret this sentence. This is confirmed when Carol is given a sentence like 'Before you move the boat, move the car'. Carol will usually misinterpret it because she would apply the order-of-mention strategy and come up with the following interpretation: 'Move boat then car'. But Carol, like Geoffrey, can use her world knowledge to override the errors produced. If sentences contain sequences of events which are highly familiar to Carol like 'Before you go to bed, brush your teeth', this familiarity overrides the order-of-mention principle and she will interpret the sentence correctly. Once again, this does not mean that she has mastery of 'Before' but that what we say, how we say it and when we say it influences her comprehension.

Children like Geoffrey and Carol show language difficulties which are most evident in their comprehension. It should be emphasised that because these children's language problems centre around comprehension, this does not mean that they do not have any difficulty with the productive aspects of language. Indeed, problems in comprehension and production of language are intimately related.

What can we then do to help Geoffrey and Carol? The first step has already been taken by careful analysis of the strategies they use to aid their comprehension. We know that

Geoffrey relies on the typical-order strategy and uses his world knowledge to override this strategy when appropriate. Carol, we know, relies on the order-of-mention strategy and uses her familiarity with everyday routines to override this strategy when necessary.

What we need to do next is to slowly help Geoffrey and Carol to learn to process structures without over-reliance on the strategies, the situation, familiarity and world knowledge. Thus the school curriculum for Geoffrey and Carol must include activities aimed at fostering their ability to focus on specific linguistic structures and their meaning. The SCORE contrasting principle is of particular importance here. A child like Geoffrey, for example, would benefit from comparing and contrasting active and passive sentence structures. At first the teacher would guide Geoffrey as to what specific aspects to focus on. She needs to clearly formulate the contrast between the structures before children like Geoffrey can begin to understand how their meaning is derived. With older children like Geoffrey and Carol, reading and writing can be used to enhance oral language. Reading and writing afford the chance for the child to spend time to reflect about the structure he is trying to interpret. Oral language is heard sequentially and thus puts a special demand on auditory memory and temporal processing. In contrast, written language is presented 'ready made' and in total, thus allowing the child to scan, review and analyse. Reading and writing also provide a medium for the practice of rules and increased automaticity. It is not always the case that language is learned through speech alone. Literacy skills, such as reading and writing, provide an important vehicle for language learning. (This aspect of language teaching is discussed more fully in Ch. 9, p. 97.)

So far in this chapter we have discussed the organisation of words into meaningful language without much reference to the psychological factors which might influence children's organisational abilities. In the next three sections we will see how children's conceptual skills, memory and capacity for attention can affect their processing of the grammatical features of language.

Conceptual/verbal reasoning problems

Language development requires the close integration of all our mental activities with our language processes. In this way we can say what we mean, and in language development during school years we see children becoming increasingly able to express their inner mental world. Their language becomes less rooted in the here and now and makes reference to all that they 'know'. Furthermore, language becomes the most important medium not only of expressing thoughts but also of the formation and organisation of the child's knowledge.

As we grow up we are exposed to many systems of knowledge. We encounter different school subjects and topics within these subjects. We form new personal relationships, and these develop their own histories of mutual experience. We will develop an understanding of our culture through hobbies, sports, films, jokes, as well as the world of books, which presents a vast potential range of mental experiences to the child. All this knowledge fits into a network of interrelated concepts and propositions. These concepts and propositions are the building blocks of thought and are coded into words, phrases, clauses, sentences, as well as larger text units of language – our concepts usually being expressed in the smaller units, words and phrases and ideas or propositions appearing as sentences and clauses. The way we weave these together into sequences which make sense is revealed by the way we put sentences together to argue, describe, persuade, and so on.

Linking sentences together successfully to express relationships between different concepts and ideas is a skill which school aims to develop to the full. But what of the child whose language problems place severe restrictions on the expression and comprehension of the simple and more basic units of thought? Consider the example of David.

David is a 7-year-old child who is receiving intensive help in a language unit because of his problem understanding language. David had an uneventful birth history with the exception that he was born jaundiced. All motor and development milestones were normal. David developed intelligible speech and his sound system was normal. None the less, his parents noticed that David sometimes failed to understand what was said to him. He was referred for assessment and his performance was found to be well within the normal range in non-verbal tests of intelligence, but in the area of language comprehension he was found to perform below the normal range.

The following is a section of a conversation between David and his teacher. In a small room in David's school the child and the teacher are looking at pictures and have a talk.

(1)   Teacher: And what do we do when we go to a dentist? What is a dentist for?
(2)   David: Ehm ... I've been to see Doctor Foster.
(3)   Teacher: For what?
(4)   David: Doctor Foster.
(5)   Teacher: Doctor Foster?
(6)   David: Yeah. Doctor Foster.
(7)   Teacher: Doctor Foster is a dentist, but what is a dentist for?
(8)   David: For teeth.
(9)   Teacher: For teeth?
(10) David: Yeah
(11) Teacher: What does he do with the teeth?
(12) David: Go to the dentist.

This type of dialogue is typical for David and it exemplifies the types of difficulties he has in understanding language. On turns 2 and 4 David gives *stereotyped responses*; that is, he provides the listener with the name of his doctor whenever a question related to the topic arises. In turn number 12 David is *responding to one word only instead of the whole question*. He has his attention on the word 'teeth' of turn 11 and thus answers with the inappropriate response of 'Go to the dentist'. Notice that David can give perfectly appropriate answers to questions that he *does* understand and always speaks appropriately when he starts the conversation. His social interaction is normal, he plays and mixes well with other children and is confident in his relationship with adults.

The next section of dialogue further exemplifies David's difficulties with understanding language. David and the

teacher are in a small room in the school and have just
finished sequencing a story about 'going to the toilet'. David
is retelling it.

(1) David: Wipe bottom, poo gone, pull chain and
                wash hands *(pointing at each picture)*.
(2) Teacher: Yes and why do you have to wash your
                hands?
(3) David: With soap.
(4) Teacher: You wash them with soap, yes. But why do
                we need to wash our hands?
(5) David: Might get germs in me hands.
(6) Teacher: That's right. Yes 'cause your mummy and
                you talked about that, didn't you? It is very
                important.

In this example, turn 3 illustrates David's inability to cope
with the abstract 'why' question. Since he is not able to
understand the 'why' question, he replies to it as if it were at
the simple level of a 'what' question. Turns 4 and 5 illustrate
the finding that David benefits from having difficult questions
repeated to him. It is our belief that this allows David some
extra time to process and understand all the words in the
question.

Both the classroom teacher and the speech therapist have
worked very closely in helping David. Together they are
helping David by providing him with language which is at a
level that he can understand. Following the order principle of
the SCORE model, they are gradually introducing more
complex concepts such as simple causality, 'why' questions
and sequences of events. They are helping David by
explaining these concepts to him, acting them out using
gestures, as well as language and setting up classroom
situations where the opportunities for David to use language
to work things out are maximised.

The example shows David using his knowledge of frames
of reference, or schemata, such as 'it's about washing' or 'it's
about the dentist'. These higher-order frames are used in
normal language-processing to help interpret the meaning of
words and phrases. Knowing that the frame is about
'dentists' gives the word 'chair' a particular referential
meaning, and the more knowledge of these frames David has

then the more they can help him overcome his conceptual difficulties. In terms of our SCORE model, David needs to experience real situations in which the smaller units of language are given meaningful usage.

David's conceptual difficulties present him with problems in understanding the links between sentences which make language appear cohesive. For example, the understanding of certain kinds of relations between words will be often assumed by competent speakers and listeners. In linking sentences we assume understanding of relationships between words such as

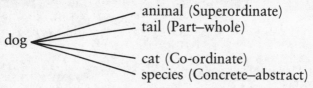

Understanding the link between two sentences such as 'The dog was hungry' and 'Animals are so demanding' necessitates knowing the part–whole relationship between dog and animal.

With a child like David an important part of his teaching will be designed to make explicit conceptual relations that underlie the meaning of words and phrases, and to link these meanings to larger situation specific frames of reference. As suggested earlier the difficulties David has at the conceptual level of language usage will lead to difficulties in processing the larger units of language which express organised thought. Unfortunately for David the essential purpose of most of the language he hears will be to express ideas and attitudes which involve relationships between concepts. And his sense of understanding this language will be seriously impaired.

The influence of memory on grammatical problems

People are more successful at remembering language when they are focusing on its meaning than when they concentrate on the sounds produced. This can be interpreted to mean that language can be processed more or less deeply, with deeper processing helping memory more than shallower or surface processing. For the normal population identification of the sound patterns of language is not in itself a problem. For many language-disabled children, however, the correct identification of the 'words' heard will be of such an order of difficulty as to demand much of their attention. Their 'mental set' when attempting to comprehend language will be at the level of sound identification. This will mean that these children are processing at a shallower level and will be less likely to remember what has been said or read.

The indications are that the deeper we process the information we hear then the more likely it is to be integrated with what we already know. The more integrated it is, the better it will be remembered and understood. We need to think not only of deeper processing but also how the processing makes links across our conceptual system.

Psychologists have made the distinction between short-term and long-term memory. Short-term memory is described as a limited store in which information is retained for a short period during which other mental operations (e.g. classification) can be carried out on this information. Then, if required, the meaning of the information can be analysed and transferred to long-term memory. Once the meaning has been extracted, the precise form of the information in short-term memory will be erased. There is a difference in skill between being able to immediately repeat language verbatim and being able to recall, using different words with equivalent meaning, what was said several hours or days previously. For most people memory is not a mental process with fixed capacity; even the well-known task of hearing and then repeating sequences of digits often used as a measure of short-term memory is 'teachable'. Extensive training on this task has improved memory from the typical 7 (plus or minus 2) digits up to as much as 80. However such training does not improve memory in general, and it is perhaps more useful to think of memory as a set of strategies which are more or less appropriate to the information being remembered. Different strategies would be required for remembering different types of information. For example the strategies used to remember digits would be different from those strategies used to remember the names of prime ministers.

Language-disabled children exhibit strategic difficulties in remembering language. For example, it has been shown that they do not make full use of organisational principles when they are asked to recall stories. They seem to focus on trying to recall individual sentences. In contrast, normal children's recall of stories focuses on the way the events link together to provide an overall theme. Their recall of stories is usually helped by being given prior instructions like, 'I want you to tell me who you like most in the story'. It seems that language-disabled children need to learn to approach stories and other texts with those organisational devices which force them to link up and contrast particular sentences so as to extract the thematic properties of language.

Linking back to the conceptual problems experienced by children like David, we know that the superordinate categories of our conceptual system assist memory. If we have words like 'chair', 'bed' and 'lamp' organised under headings like 'furniture', we will find it easier to remember them. We develop a hierarchy of systematic *contrasts* which assist recognition and recall. The language-disabled child must be helped to develop this system through techniques which make *explicit* reference to these links between words.

In addition to conceptually based categorising, other techniques like paying attention to the rhyming properties of words and forming acronyms (like SCORE) can be built into the school curriculum. These techniques have been shown to be useful for children at 8 years and above.

Peter, the next case example, shows a child whose memory difficulties will also be helped by the type of organised teaching of word relationships suggested for David. The important additional component of Peter's teaching will focus on his capacity to hold the language he has heard for long enough in his short-term memory for his coding system to operate. He must be taught to rehearse language so as to maintain it for coding. Without disregarding the situation principle, language imitation and repetition tasks will be an important part of his teaching. These will include games involving repeating all or part of words and/or sentences, rhyming games at the sound and word level as well as games involving imitation of intonation patterns such as those associated with questions and statements. These techniques are designed to ease his difficulty with short-term memory of language. Rehearsal of language in its organised (coded, chunked or clustered) form will aid the transfer of meaning to long-term memory.

Memory is also subject to situational variation. A phenomenon known as 'state-dependent memory' indicates that when we are put into the same situation where something was learned then we are more likely to remember it. The most striking experimental evidence for this showed that word lists learned underwater were remembered best when the people were put back into that situation. This phenomenon tells us that effective use of memory in classrooms or remedial clinics does not mean that it necessarily carries over to other contexts. As mentioned before, as far as memory is concerned, the *situation* aspect of the SCORE model is very important.

Let's now turn to the case of Peter. Peter is a 6-year-old child who is receiving intensive help in a language unit because he has severe problems understanding language. Peter had an uneventful birth history but experienced in the first few years of his life runny ears and glue ear, which often affected his hearing temporarily. At present Peter has normal hearing in both ears and does not suffer from middle ear problems as frequently. Peter's fine and gross motor control are quite good: he is able to copy quite accurately and 'colour in' neatly. He is also very agile and is able to work on large PE apparatus confidently. In formal tests of ability Peter performs in the low average range non-verbally, though it is also evident that he has severe memory problems (4th percentile in auditory memory and 6th percentile in visual memory as measured by the *British Ability Scales* – Elliot, Murray and Pearson, 1983).

Following is a section of a conversation between Peter and his teacher. Child and teacher are in a corner of the classroom having a chat.

(1) Teacher: What do you do when you've lost something?

(2) Peter: Tooth (*pointing to his mouth*).

(3) Teacher: You've got some more teeth coming through up there, haven't you?

(4) Peter: Look (*showing gums*).

   (5) Teacher: But Peter, what do you do when you've lost
                     something?
   (6) Peter: Tooth ... tooth out.
   (7) Teacher: You've lost your tooth!
   (8) Peter: Yes.
   (9) Teacher: Yes, I see.

This type of dialogue exemplifies the typical type of difficulties Peter has in understanding utterances which are long: he cannot retain them long enough in memory to process them. In turn 2 Peter is answering the question as if he were asked, 'You've lost something?' Peter is only attending to the last bit of the question and thus his response is inappropriate. Even after repetition of the question at turn 5, Peter continues to answer inappropriately.

Peter's memory difficulties affect all aspects of his language but most noticeably comprehension. At the level of sound contrasts, Peter's phonology is variable and breaks down in longer utterances. It is as if Peter forgets the target sounds he needs to produce to say a word. He sometimes drops a whole syllable and calls toilet 'toi' and trousers 'trous'. His syntax is also affected by his memory difficulties. Peter usually uses short utterances. The length of utterances that Peter produces is related to the length of utterance he can understand.

The classroom teacher and the speech therapist have worked together to design a programme which will help Peter develop strategies to compensate and improve his memory. In the classroom Peter is consistently talked to with short enough sentences so that he can understand and feel the reward of successful communication. Following the order principle of the SCORE model, individual work with Peter has concentrated on helping him understand an increasing number of information-carrying words (italics below) in utterances. For example:

Very simple level: Pick the *knife*
                       Pick the *spoon*

Simple level: Pick the *little knife*
                       Pick the *red ball*

Complex: Put the *knife on* the *chair*
                 Put the *spoon under* the *table*

More complex: Put the *baby under* the *little bed*
                 Put the *knife behind* the *red chair*

Activities have also involved categorisation and association of objects and actions as it is hoped that the association of everyday sequences of events will help Peter's memory. If he has to recall unrelated items, each item takes a bit of memory space no matter how small that item is. On the other hand, if items are associated or related, they together take one bit of memory, therefore increasing his potential for processing longer utterances. The work done with Peter's understanding of language is affecting his production of language and thus his utterances are increasing in length. This also lends support to Peter being categorised as a child with problems *understanding* language as it is through working on his language understanding that other aspects of language are improving.

Attentional problems and language difficulties

We need to attend to the language we hear in a way that selects it out from all the other simultaneous perceptions with which our world bombards us. This process of selective attention is necessary because of our limitations in the simultaneous processing of information. We can only organise and understand the meaning of a limited amount of new sensory perceptions at any one time.

There is good evidence that some parts of a brain play an important part in the directing of attention. It has been suggested that attention is an evolutionary development from a more primitive sleep–wake arousal system. When we are attending effectively, our brain structures are 'tuned' to process information more effectively. We cannot, of course, consider attention entirely independently of motivation and our brains are pre-set to find certain kinds of stimulation rewarding. Perceptual experiences which provide such stimulation are more likely to be attended to than those which generate no effects within the nerve cells controlling our reward–punishment systems.

The theoretical link between the complex and subtle rewards of human conversation and more primitive motivators such as food, water and sun remains to be explained. But attention to human language requires some motivating force to engage the child's language processes, and some children require considerable help at the level of initial and continuous engagement with the problem of decoding language. Consider the example of Paul. At the age of 4 Paul was referred for assessment due to his parents' concern about his understanding of language. Paul was described by his parents as a child who 'flitted' from one thing to another, did not play for very long with anything and did not listen to what was said to him. They had difficulty having Paul following their instructions and they began to wonder if Paul may have specific problems. Paul's early history was relatively uneventful. Paul had no birth complications, he walked at 16 months and had a febrile fit at 2 years of age. Since the fit at 2 there have not been any further fits and thus the suggestion of epilepsy has been ruled out. Paul's performance in non-verbal tests of ability has consistently shown that he is a child of average abilities with no other specific problems except attention.

At the age of 5 Paul was placed in a language unit in an ordinary school in the hope that intensive work on his attention and cutting out external stimuli such as noise would gradually help him transfer to an ordinary school setting. The language unit teacher, the speech therapist and staff described Paul as a child who had great difficulty in concentrating his attention and cutting out external stimuli such as noise inside and outside the classroom. Together they devised a school and home programme to improve his attentional skills. Following are a few examples of the goals and techniques of Paul's individual programme.

Working on attentional skills

(1) Following the encouragement principle of the SCORE model, establish a structured and enjoyable working method to provide Paul with motivation and reinforcement:

(a) In a natural situation achieve reliable selection of objects by:
– function (get the one we brush our teeth with)
– description (give me the long, blue one).

(b) In a natural (e.g. play) situation achieve reliable use of objects. For example, comb hair with comb; brush teeth with toothbrush.

(c) In natural interaction, model and encourage sequences of play. For example, washing dolls sequence, having tea sequence.

(2) Following the order principle of the SCORE model, have Paul carry out increasingly more complex verbal instructions. For example,
Pick up the knife. Pick up the long knife.
Pick up the long knife and put it on the chair.

(3) Following the regularity principle of the SCORE model, establish a link between class activities and home activities:

(a) Sit together and go over picture books. Read short stories.

(a) Develop a story before bed routine.

(b) Sequencing of stories and routine events.

(b) Have Paul participate and describe routine sequences such as setting table before eating, running the water and getting toys ready before bath time.

(c) Have a scrapbook of things that go together; for example, things of the same colour, things that we eat.

(c) Same scrapbook is taken home over the weekend and shared with family and in addition a new set of things that go together is made.

After a year and a half in the language unit Paul could concentrate well in tasks and understand language like children his own age, though he remained a distractible child. He was then gradually transferred to a small class in his local school.

The subsequent school curriculum for Paul must include tasks aimed at fostering his ability to attend to and monitor his own performance. Conscious monitoring tasks must be built into his school work; for example, 'Make a mark with your crayon whenever you hear the name of an animal in this list.' Of course, any attempt to encourage listening must bear in mind that one does not listen to what one cannot understand.

The development of self-testing procedures which show the child the use of questions like 'Do I know this?' 'How much do I know?' and 'What does it mean?' These need to be explicitly formulated within normal lessons by the teacher before children like Paul will see their practical function.

Paul's problems will be very clearly seen when he is in control of the rate at which tasks are done. Self-regulation is a severe problem for him, but the educational answer is not to avoid these tasks. Paul should be given things he can do reasonably easily but which take a period of time, which extends his capacity for self-regulation.

Standard approaches to grammatical disabilities

The grammatical problems discussed so far in this chapter have focused on younger children. But, as we have already said, many language-disabled children are to be found throughout the school population. These children will experience some problems with each new type of linguistic complexity that they are required to use. And school does place more and more emphasis on complex forms of language as children grow older.

For the remainder of this chapter we will outline some of the standard procedures available to teachers to help children master those complex constructions which they often find difficult. The principles underlying all those approaches are those outlined in the SCORE model in Chapter 4. These principles combined with the examples which follow should be enough to show how further techniques can be tried.

However, we recommend the well-known book by Elizabeth Wiig and Eleanor Semel, *Language Assessment and Intervention for the Learning Disabled*, for additional examples.

The procedures discussed in the remainder of the chapter are designed to give children practice at operating the grammatical rules of language. By working through specific examples coupled with explanations of the principles involved, language-disabled children can be helped to build up the grammar that comes naturally to most children. It is our intuitive knowledge of the workings of grammar which allows strings of words to make sense. Of course, this knowledge is not conscious, and unless we have taken course in linguistics we will be unable to make it explicit. It is perhaps the most complex form of intuitive knowledge we possess, but it is perhaps most clearly revealed when the language-disabled children, who lack it, are studied and taught. The techniques which follow attempt to simplify the acquisition of grammar for these children by working with units of language which concentrate on one important feature of grammar at a time. These will be no substitute for hard work on these tasks and much practice will be required. At all times the relationship between change in meaning and change in grammar must be made clear. There is no point in teaching meaningless linguistic tricks to children. Transfer of these techniques into classroom activities is the exciting and rewarding task of the teacher and constitutes part of overall curriculum planning. This book does not directly tackle the design of an overall curriculum for the language-disabled; we are focusing on the language problems. However, useful ideas can be found in Ella Hutt's interesting book *Teaching Language-Disabled Children: A Structured Curriculum*. This book deals with children in a special school with the freedom to base their entire education around severe language difficulties. The teacher of special-needs children in ordinary schools faces different problems of class and pupil management. The techniques which follow are usable and effective in this setting when integrated into the curriculum designated for the children concerned.

Cloze Procedure and Sentence Completion

Both Cloze Procedure and Sentence Completion set a

sentence frame with one or more words deleted. Cloze Procedure may involve a series of such deletions whereas sentence completion leaves the child to fill in the gap at the end of a sentence. Both techniques are useful at all the levels of language – words, sentence and text. They are particularly suitable for revealing the way in which appropriate word choice is governed by what has come before. For example: The woman was clever. She thought very (slowly, quickly, quicker).

Deletion procedures can be varied according to mode of presentation (oral or written) and the extent to which the children are given options from which to choose. They may be left to fill the gaps using their own language. The great strength of these methods is to allow the teacher to focus the child on to one particular feature of language at a time. The SCORE principle of *contrast* is easily built into the task via both the multiple choices and the actual sentence frames. For example. Paul gave Mary a present – thanked him (he/she); Mary gave Paul a present – thanked her (he/she).

Unscrambling language
The grammar of English is expressed by the order of words in sentences. One useful way of engaging children's attention on word order is to give them collections of words to arrange into the correct order. This can be done at both the phrase and sentence level.
For example:

Phrase level:	The man thin tall. (The tall thin man)
Sentence level:	Gave him away who. (Who gave him away?)

Changing the mood and voice
In English we can express changes of mood between question, statement and instruction by small changes either in word order or omission and insertion of words. Tasks can be developed around language, which shows the child the skill of interchanging sentences like:

Statement: (1) The man is talking to the girl.

Question: (2) Is the man talking to the girl?

Instruction: (3) Talk to the girl.

The relation between active and passive voice can be dealt with in the same way. Passive: (4) The girl is being talked to by the man. Changes into negative form can also be made clear by structuring these contrasts according to the SCORE model. It is very important that tasks such as those above are not turned into a drill which is unrelated to the child's real experiences. The successful teacher should be able to introduce these contrasts when an opportunity arises in the context of classroom life. For example, teachers often require children to paraphrase language; to repeat what has been said, or read, in their own words. These paraphrasing tasks will often include changes of mood and voice and the teacher can focus attention on the occasions when they do.

Combining simple sentences into complex ones

The many ways that the language of education makes use of complex sentences expressing subordinate and relative clause relationships are discussed in Chapter 8. It is very useful to provide children with structured opportunities to construct complex sentence propositions. For example, 'The giraffe chased the hippo. The hippo ran quickly away' becomes one of 'The giraffe chased the hippo who/but/and ran quickly away'. This type of procedure can be reversed by asking children to resolve complex sentences into simple propositions.

Understanding morphology

English morphology refers to those suffixes and prefixes which indicate grammatical and semantic distinctions such as, tense, number, possessives, comparatives, adverbs, and so on.

Because these elements of language are both short, and typically attached to other words whose meaning they modify, they present particular problems to the learning-disabled child. Some elements of English morphology follow regular rules or patterns, other elements are exceptions to these rules (the plural of sheep is not sheeps).

Particular areas of difficulty are agreement between:

– Plural nouns and plural verbs.
– Irregular tenses of verbs: run → ran (not runned).
– Plural subjects and plural objects: The men ate their apple(s).
– Adverbs and verbs: The man runs/running regularly.
– Nouns derived from verbs: begin/beginner, and exceptions like cook/cooker.

Teaching the question form

There are in English many ways which the question form takes. There are all the 'wh' question types: what, which, who, why, when and where. Other questions are simply formed by reversal of word order; for example, 'He is kind' – 'Is he kind?.'

The use of verbal auxiliaries like 'can' and 'will' also forms questions if they are put in the right slot in the sentence. These, and other variants such as 'how', can be taught in a number of different ways. Of particular use again is the technique of paraphrase. It is very helpful to teach children to ask the same question in different ways, for example, what is the name of your teacher – Who is your teacher. The basic approach to question teaching is to structure the question around possible answers. Questions make no sense to children if they have no sense of what an answer might look like.

Dealing with ambiguity

Sentence ambiguity is often resolved by the contexts in which the language occurs. However, ambiguous sentences can be very useful in building up an awareness of language. There is much humour potential to be gained from the plays on words surrounding ambiguity. Phrases with idiomatic and concrete meanings like 'jump at' as in 'jump at the chance' versus 'jump at the noise', are an example of this ambiguity. Another source of ambiguity comes from the many words which have more than one meaning. These lend themselves to 'contrast' tasks as in 'Give me the light one' in the context of toys which have different shades and weights.

Overview

In this short section we have indicated some of the many features of grammar and related aspects of language which lend themselves to direct teaching with school-age language-disabled children. As suggested earlier, Wiig and Semel (1984) give more detailed examples, and we refer the reader to this work for more detailed guidance. However, we have also mentioned that the *situation* principle of the SCORE model would lead to an integration of these techniques into the child's typical language experiences.

7

Conversational Disabilities and Communication Skills

What we say, how we say it and to whom are all important aspects of communication. Speakers and listeners can choose different ways to communicate; they may have an argument or tell a story or describe an important past experience. Each different type of communication has its own 'rules' which children have to learn.

Furthermore, we need to know which conversational act to perform; for example, whether to agree, argue, qualify, and so on. We must be able to participate at the right moment and know how to do this. And we must choose our words and sentences so that we are relevant and clear to our audience. In all these areas a skilled conversational partner who, for example, explains an ambiguity or clarifies our own statements can make us appear better at communicating than we might otherwise be. And children's success at communicating depends very much on the support they receive from adults and older children.

The term 'pragmatics' is often used to encompass those aspects of language use which are subject to systematic variation according to the social context. Children with severe problems in recognising and satisfying the social rules of language are usually described as having pragmatic or conversational disabilities. They will often fail to see how the intentions behind the communication are related to linguistic forms to suit different situations and to convey different personal styles. The utterance 'Have you seen Mary?' demands more than 'Yes' as an answer but conveys subtly different implications from 'Where's Mary?'. The latter conveying, in general, more directness, urgency and assumptions about the listener's knowledge. Even at the level of pronoun usage ('he' or 'she' versus 'Peter' or 'Mary') and the choice of definite (the) and indefinite article (a, an) we imply knowledge, or the lack of it, on the part of listeners. '*He* did it' assumes 'He' is known and '*The* book is on the table' refers to a book the listener knows about. These examples draw our attention to the complex system involved in conversation.

As competent conversationalists we are also able to select utterances which, while they may be equivalent in meaning when taken out of context, have different effects when produced in a real social situation. Take for example the utterance 'It is hot in here'. Out of context, it appears that this utterance has a clear meaning. But it can be used either to comment on the room temperature or as an *indirect request* for someone to open the window. This example shows that exactly the same words can have different functions depending on the context, and this is something the child has to learn.

Thus, in the area of pragmatics we no longer think in terms of words or word combinations to form utterances but we think in terms of the communicative acts and strategies children perform when *using* language. Because of this, one of the areas we need to pay attention to is how utterances function in social contexts and particularly what children can and cannot do with words. Table 7.1 provides a list of *some* of the communicative acts we perform in everyday conversation. We can use this table as a guide to assess the type of communicative acts language-disabled children may fail to use effectively. It is known that language-disabled children have particular difficulties requesting information or clarification from their conversational partner. The language-disabled child may receive an ambiguous command or request, and instead of requesting more information or clarification, the child tends to try to respond as best he can with what he has heard. In other words, language-disabled children are known to have very poor strategies for repairing conversations, and this is an area where they need practice and help. The framework of functions of utterances provides us with some of the key areas necessary for adequate conver-

Table 7.1   Conversational acts

Act	Definition	Example
Requests	Solicit information or actions.	More juice please. My turn?
Responses	Supply solicited information.	It fall. Yes, it is.
Directives	Order or prompt.	Go there! Move over!
Comments	Make statements about a particular state of affairs.	I already did that. It fell on the floor.
Informing	Stating what is not readily observable.	You can go sideways. He can't get out that way.
Reasoning	Offering a justification for an action or opinion.	Because I like it. Don't play with it because it's broken.
Predicting	Anticipating outcomes.	If you hit me, I'll tell the teacher. You'll be sorry if you lose it.
Evaluating	Offering personal judgements.	That's naughty. Your work is very good today.
Suggesting	Recommending information or a course of action.	You should try to finish it before lunch. Let's go together tomorrow.
Joking	Offering information which is incongruous or false to cause a humorous effect.	While you were in the bathroom, the teacher said we have to do 100 more lines. Your trousers have ripped.

sational development, and very often language-disabled children need teaching in most of these areas. Following the situation principle of the SCORE model, teachers need to develop programmes in which language-disabled children can learn to use conversational acts appropriately.

In addition, in normal development, the way in which we express meaning in words we use takes account of the context and the conversational demands of the situation. The way we learn how to do this is presumably through some well rehearsed, largely unconscious procedures or high-level schemata. These procedures are acquired through our conversation experience and become part of the organising principles of our communication. But as mentioned before conversationally disabled children do not develop these procedures naturally. They cannot always adequately meet the conversational demands of the situation and what they say often appears inappropriate, irrelevant or unclear. In other words, they have problems in introducing and maintaining topics appropriately. The brief anecdote of Samantha can illustrate this point. One morning during assembly, Samantha put her hand up. The headmaster asked Samantha what she wanted and she said, 'I have had my period today'. A profound silence followed, Samantha was unable to sort out when it was appropriate to talk about certain topics and when it was not. She was very pleased to have reached this stage in maturity and she wanted to share it with everybody! Topic introduction and maintenance is another area of pragmatics many language-disabled children need help in. But many children have subtler problems than Samantha. In the ordinary class they may appear rather shy, withdrawn and not very talkative. Peers and adults may describe them as 'loners'. Spontaneous conversations with them are rather awkward; their pausing may be too long or too short. They may only give you minimal answers and they may not follow your line of thought very well. The range of conversational acts they use may be very restricted, only responding when drawn into conversation by an adult. Also, when language requires inference, as in making a joke or reasoning, the child may appear to not quite understand beyond the literal meaning of words. These children for whom communication and social interaction is difficult, need to be drawn into peer partnerships/friendships and shown in many cases, through role play and modelling, how to behave and communicate with other children as well as adults. Following are two case examples of children with marked conversational disabilities which illustrate the history, assessment and remediation typical of such children.

Kevin is a 15-year-old young man who attends an open-air school for delicate children. Kevin is withdrawn to a language unit for one hour every day. Kevin had no problems at birth nor subsequently as a toddler. His mother described him as a very good baby, very easy to take care of and no trouble to have around. He was toilet trained at 18 months and could eat with a knife and fork very early. His speech and language development was delayed: he only had a handful of words at the age of 3. His mother worried about this and referred him for speech therapy. When she described her concerns about Kevin to the speech therapist, she kept on pointing out that he was not like other 3-year-olds. He did not get involved in play with children his age, he did not run after them or seek the company of other children nor did he draw attention to things around him in order to share interest with adults and peers. For example, Kevin did not bring toys or things for his mother to see. He was assessed non-verbally and was found to perform within the low range of abilities. His hearing and vision were normal, but his language was delayed and his play of very poor quality.

Following is a portion of dialogue between Kevin and a language unit friend while in play. Kevin was 10-years-old at the time. Below he is talking with a classmate in a quiet, small room with toys.

(1) Classmate: *(Playing having dinner)* What do you want?

(2) Kevin: Fish and chips *(pretends to eat with a fork)*.

(3) Classmate: Cup of tea.
                    Cup of tea there *(pointing to cups and saucers)*.

(4) Kevin: Finish chips.

(5) Classmate: *(Brings cake to eat with tea)* Cut it half. Share it, cut equal.

(6) Kevin: Not share chips.

Though Kevin was 10 in this dialogue and had received considerable help with play, he still remained passive as a playing partner. He did not initiate play (unless coaxed) but instead waited for someone else to set up the scenario and ask him to join in. His social behaviour towards other children or adults was naïve and as a result he had no friends at school.

As time passed, it has become clearer that Kevin's problems are mostly related to social/communicative interaction. Kevin had difficulty working out what information would be needed to cope with a given situation (e.g. finding a certain item in a supermarket; making arrangements to meet over the telephone; reassuring someone who is worried); he has difficulty adapting his language to fit the needs of the listener (telling a classmate how to play a game that he knows but the classmate does not); he has difficulty grasping which points are relevant and important and how one relates to another. Furthermore, he had difficulty initiating and maintaining a conversation – his conversations are halting, difficult, contain long pauses, minimum initiations and poor topic maintenance.

Following is a portion of dialogue between Kevin and his old teacher/therapist. Kevin is 15-years-old in the scene below. The teacher/therapist comes to visit the school and has not seen Kevin for six months. They go together to a quiet room and have a chat.

(1) Teacher: I haven't been here for a long time, have I?

(2) Kevin: No *(12-second pause)*.

(3) Teacher: Do you want to know what happened to me?

(4) Kevin: What happened?

(5) Teacher: Oh, I don't come here anymore. I am going to a school in the village I live.

(6) Kevin: Yes.

(7) Teacher: I go there a few days a week.

(8) Kevin: Yes *(5-second pause)*.

(9) Teacher: How are things at home?

(10) Kevin: Alright.

(11) Teacher: Have you been doing much at home?

(12) Kevin: Cooking breakfast for myself.

(13) Teacher: Oh, Kevin, that is excellent. What sort of things are you doing?

(14) Kevin: Scrambled eggs and beans.

(15) Teacher: Super. I'd like you to come and make my breakfast at home.

(16) Kevin: Yes *(Seriously)*

(17) Teacher: It would be nice for me, wouldn't it? *(laughs)*.

(18) Kevin: Yes *(seriously)*.

(19) Teacher: Hum.

It can be seen that Kevin allows for long pauses between turns in conversation (see turns 2 and 8). He also has great difficulty initiating conversation and understanding humour (see turns 15–16). Conversations are awkward, and his minimal responses make it very difficult for the dialogue to move forward.

The classroom teacher, language unit teacher and speech therapist in consultation with other multidisciplinary professionals involved with the school have developed a programme to help Kevin develop strategies to cope with social/communicative interactions. The programme emphasises verbal reasoning as it relates to social skills – that is, getting Kevin to see he needs to think about people and events, to plan things and predict outcomes. A great amount of role play is being used to practice routine sequences of events such as going shopping and ordering food in a cafeteria. In addition, Kevin is encouraged to analyse his own social/communicative behaviour and shape it. He is told explicitly after a conversation what things he has done that could be improved, such as, 'You did not ask *me* any questions this time', 'You did not tell me what you liked', or he watches himself on a video and analyzes his performance. Kevin is advised on how to change his verbal/non-verbal behaviours, and a lot of practice and modelling follow. It is very hard for Kevin to exactly follow what he is simply told to do. It works much better if he is told and shown (modelling).

Let's now turn to the case of Tony. Tony is an 11-year-old child who has conspicuous difficulties using language for social interaction. Tony was born with forceps after a long labour. He was a placid baby and his parents report he was no trouble to look after. He did not demand attention and he appeared to lack interest in human company. Tony uttered his first words at 2 years of age, did not exhibit any deviant pattern (no echolalia) but appeared socially withdrawn. He attended local mainstream education and then transferred to a school for children with learning difficulties. Tony did not cope well in this school and began to develop bizarre behaviours such as laughing hysterically for no reason. He was transferred part-time to a special class for children (in the same school) but eventually was taken to a psychiatric unit. After a year in the unit Tony was finally placed at a boarding school for children with special needs. Tony is a child of average intelligence that presents with a large discrepancy between his verbal and non-verbal skills. Tony finds it very difficult to use language to reason through abstract events and situations and to use language in conversation and in interaction with people.

Tony appears as a child with little facial expression and infrequent eye contact, though he sometimes earnestly looks into a person's face as if looking for the meaning that eludes him. Tony has developed very good mechanical reading abilities, though he has great difficulty understanding what he reads. His mathematical ability is excellent as well as his spelling and handwriting. When writing narratives or descriptions, Tony has difficulty organising his ideas, making cause and effect links, providing reasons for events, and so on. In general, Tony has problems making sense of experience. Following is an example of Tony's story writing:

I am a cat. I live in the playground around the meadow. I am a
persian siamese cat. I am a red and green cat. I drink milk. I eat cat
food and I eat it all. I am Peter. My name is Peter, I know my name. I
am a lucky cat. I like milk. I drink milk all. I know what I drink. I
know what I eat. I eat good cat food. I know where I live. I know
what colours I am. I know what colours I like. I like red and green. I
sleep in a windy place.

                                                    (Tony at 10:6 years)

Tony has an excellent rote memory and excels in board
games such as chess. None the less, he is not perceived as
equal by his classroom peers. They tend to look after him and
let adults know if anything is amiss with him. He has no
friends and his social behaviour is naïve. He does not seem to
be able to adapt what he says to fit the needs of others: he has
a very hard time putting himself in the perspective of the
listener. He often ignores or misinterprets non-verbal signs
(such as facial expression, gestures) from both his peers and
adults. He does not understand jokes made by peers, though
sometimes he can appreciate literal simple humour. His
conversations with peers and adults are stilted. He rarely
initiates conversation, may change the topic of conversation
abruptly and would much rather get on with 'his own thing'
than interact with another person. Following is an example
of dialogue with Tony. The teacher and Tony are having a
chat in a corner of the classroom.

(1) Teacher: What did you do over the holidays, Tony?

(2) Tony: I went to watch 'Snow White and the Seven
               Dwarfs'.

(3) Teacher: Was it good?

(4) Tony: I hope so ... *(looking away)*. It was ...
               it was *(rather worried)*.

(5) Teacher: Can you remember the story?

(6) Tony: I can't think of it.

(7) Teacher: No ...

(8) Tony: That's why *(rather upset)*.

Tony may get quite upset at his own inability to make sense of experience and to communicate about it. The programme to help Tony is aimed mainly at improving his verbal-reasoning abilities and to improve his social/communicative skills. Following the order principle in the SCORE model, Tony had been brought down to read at a level he can understand. He is encouraged to pick any book he likes from the library (whether he can understand it or not), but he also is encouraged to read books that he can make sense of. Given Tony's excellent mechanical reading abilities, reading has concentrated on reading for meaning and understanding the sequence of events presented in the story. In addition, a large amount of role-play work has been done with Tony. Routine interactions such as going shopping, borrowing something from somebody, talking on the telephone, have been enacted and practised. All the essential steps involved in the interaction (e.g. greeting the shop owner, thanking the person from whom you borrowed something, etc.) are identified, talked about and written down in a special communication copybook. Tony can then glimpse through the copybook like an actor would his cue card before he has to go through with the interaction. Eventually, it is hoped that Tony will internalise these routines so much he will not need the 'cue cards' any more. In the case of Tony a peer has been used as an intervention agent. Tony's classroom teacher selected one of Tony's classmates who could be encouraged to try to be Tony's friend and help him. Fred was chosen because he was a kind and gentle child, he had a lot of hobbies and he liked Tony. Fred was advised to seek the company of Tony at break and lunchtime and to share his hobbies with him. Fred was also told that Tony had a hard time knowing what to say and how to behave with friends and that he needed to be told and shown what to do. It was also thought that the peer relationship needed to be supported in the classroom, so Fred and Tony were often paired for chores and they were both included in group work.

This approach benefited Tony. Fred had a lot of hobbies, among which were birds and bird-watching. At breaktimes Tony was thus drawn to bird-watching as well as kicking the ball and playing around. Tony became very interested in birds, began to read books about them and to look out for information that he could share with Fred. For Tony's teacher one of the greatest rewards was to hear Tony say to a fellow teacher, 'I have a friend now Miss'.

8

Language Disabilities in School

Schools are rich and complex language environments, but to a language-disabled child this complexity presents many unrealistic demands. The resulting sense of anxiety and inadequacy will often lead to impulsive responses which interfere with reflecting on and processing information. For example, these children will often respond to questions from teachers by word association, an inadequate strategy in instructional contexts.

However, many youngsters reach secondary education with language difficulties which have gone undetected. Large screening programmes tend only to spot the more obvious problems of younger children, not adolescents. As the task and curriculum demands increase in secondary education, these children's language problems begin to affect their classroom performance. In many ways these children give a confusing picture. Sometimes they cope, sometimes they do not. This is true not only across subjects but across time. These children's language problems may surface at one point in their school careers and not another. Similarly, they may affect particular subjects in the curriculum and not others, and language problems may seem to have been solved only to appear again as the curriculum demands increase.

Language is often undervalued because it is not a curriculum subject. This situation worsens as the child moves to secondary education where there is a great deal of subject compartmentalisation. Each subject in the curriculum is thought to be a group of skills that can be taught apart from language.

Recent advances in the area of communication development have clearly shown that language acquisition is not a process that ends in early childhood. Language continues to develop throughout the school years. In addition, it is thought that language interacts with the child's learning and ability to cope with the demands of the classroom. Thus those children with language difficulties do not have a discrete, contained problem. They have a problem which affects their whole school career.

There are many pitfalls awaiting these children in school. The language of teachers gets more complex as the child moves up through school and also becomes less fluent as they deal with more difficult ideas. Classrooms are also noisy places, often with poor acoustics, making the detection of the correct words very difficult for some language-disabled children. Often, important logical differences are conveyed by very small and easily undetected linguistic units, (e.g. if–then, either–or). Also teachers use many linguistic techniques for assessing knowledge (e.g. 'Spot the wrong word'). In addition, their instructions about classroom organisation and lesson planning are usually verbal. Lastly, language and general interactive style vary between different teachers.

These and many other important functions of language in school show how important it is that we develop the assessment procedures to find and help language-disabled children. One reason why large-scale screening for language at the secondary level is difficult is because the materials available are biased towards the younger child. In this chapter we suggest a solution to this problem through the development of assessment procedures which test the language demands placed on older children. For example, assessments under time constraint in distracting conditions with delayed responses and with instructions which require careful thought will reveal language difficulties. And these conditions mirror classroom life. Similarly, tests which require production of longer pieces of language will reveal problems in planning and monitoring language.

The approach to language intervention taken in this book integrates techniques directed at improving cognitive skills such as memory, attention, perception and reflection. The complex nature of language requires that it is not treated separately from other aspects of learning and development. Traditional modes of assessment have been restricted to measures such as mean length of utterance, vocabulary size and grammatical structure. Our approach acknowledges current research which shows that these linguistic measures tell only a part of the story. A fuller picture of language proficiency comes from looking at the many ways language is actually used. This means taking full account of the semantic, pragmatic and social features of communication. Also, if language remediation is to have much educational value, we need to look at the many complex uses language has in learning and development in classrooms.

As we have seen, normal language development continues throughout the school years. During this period children integrate and consolidate language skills as well as learning new aspects of language. We have described how younger children's strategies for comprehension and production develop into better tools for dealing with more complex forms of language. In particular, children become able to deal with sentences combined into narratives, arguments, instructions and many other rhetorical devices. Furthermore, these forms of discourse are processed by appropriate selection from an increasing number of strategies involving prior knowledge, contextual information and understanding of how sentences cohere together to make text intelligible.

From what is now known about the development of those skills in normal children it might be thought possible to develop a fixed set of analytical instruments which will both detect children's difficulties and automatically suggest teaching procedures. However, this is not possible for a variety of reasons; ranging from the individual nature of each child's difficulties to the variation in school environments in which children are placed. We can, however, go some way to indicate how to proceed in tackling the difficulties of the language-disabled child in a school environment.

The first problem to be faced is how to identify a child with a language difficulty. We have already argued that many problems which are at root linguistic are often seen by teachers as either academic or social problems. Particularly at secondary school level, we do not have sensitive enough screening tools which will quickly and easily identify the language-disabled child. Given that so many children's language problems are masked by their involvement in other difficulties with the curriculum, how can we improve our identification techniques in the absence of simple large-scale screening tests? The answer is fairly simple in outline but as with most educational changes both problematic and expensive in practice.

Our only way forward is through an extensive in-service education programme for teachers, about language problems, together with substantially more back-up from clinicians experienced in language pathology. These clinicians will also have to extend their current knowledge base to include a better understanding of the role of language and literacy in educational processes. In our current multi-ethnic societies the problems of cultural interactions must also be seen to go beyond basic language proficiency and into the varied, subtle and complex uses of language which the school curriculum demands.

The aim must be to assess pupils' use of language in the natural context of the classroom and to detect the points at which the pupil is failing to cope with the language demands being made. In practice, because secondary school teachers see particular pupils on average for not much more than one hour each day, they need to be highly sensitised to potential language problems. The in-service education programme must provide teachers with skills in using appropriate guidelines for identifying language difficulties. Table 8.1 illustrates a framework for guided identification of children with language difficulties.

The guidelines presented in Table 8.1 must be used with caution. Many children who are not language-disabled will on some occasions get a 'Yes' to the questions posed. The children we are trying to identify will be those who on many occasions get a 'Yes' to at least several of the questions. They will consistently, across different contexts, with different people and with no known explanation (e.g. stress due to an emotional upset) be seen to have difficulties with the facets of language illustrated in the table.

How might a teacher proceed when these guidelines suggest that a child has a language difficulty? In practice, of course, the teachers' response will be heavily constrained by

Table 8.1 Guidelines for identifying language-disabled children

---

Does the pupil:

(a) often misunderstand simple instructions either spoken or written?

(b) make errors when reading aloud?

(c) have difficulty in keeping track of conversations?

(d) find it difficult to complete unfinished sentences appropriately?

(e) rarely correctly make the adequate 'how', 'why', 'what if' and 'what next' inferences?

(f) produce odd grammatical structures when speaking and/or writing?

(g) not seem to fully understand logical connectives like 'because', 'therefore', 'so', 'if–then', 'however' and 'although'.

(h) not seem to get the gist of what has been said; not know what many things read or heard are about?

(i) have poor memory for linguistically presented information?

(j) fail to make connections between what has been read or heard?

(k) talk in a roundabout and vague way, often not completing sentences and repeating himself?

(l) becomes difficult to understand in terms of the sounds used as the language demands increase?

(m) avoid tasks and situations involving language?

(n) seem slow to respond to instructions to a group and depend on social cues?

---

the type and extent of the resources that can be called upon for help – the availability of classroom assistants, remedial teachers, language therapists and educational psychologists, as well as the degree of parental involvement that can be mobilised. Yet the basic principles of the SCORE model still apply to the action taken by the remedial team, however it may be constituted.

The child must be helped with both expressing and verbally understanding the ideas presented in the language of its classroom. Both the 'situation' and 'context' of the SCORE approach remind us that language therapy should be directed at the actual linguistic experiences the child faces and should wherever possible take place within the classroom. It may be asked whether there is any substantial differences between such an approach and any general remedial programme. The answer is that there will be similarities but also many differences. These differences arise because we cannot assume that the language-disabled child will find the same topics in the curiculum as easy or difficult as the normal child, or even the intellectually impaired child. The presence of language difficulties lends another dimension to the educational experience.

We know that the language of classrooms tends to be formal whereas language-disabled children show a strong preference for an informal style. Teacher language is often poorly organised and lacks helpful summaries of what has been said. Children are required to make sense of this language, which often mixes relevant and irrelevant information. Furthermore, evidence of understanding is often demanded in the form of written notes or essays, placing even more weight on the language skills of the child. The problems experienced by children with language difficulties will depend on the extent to which teaching, learning and assessment depend on uses of language which they have been unable to master.

We will now consider the examples of two rather different children, their language problems and how to help them. Derek is a 14-year-old boy whose school performance has markedly deteriorated over the past year. His teachers describe him as a pleasant, well-motivated child whose written work seemed to be well below the level of understanding he demonstrated in classroom discussions. The teachers commented that his written work lacked overall organisation and the links between individual sentences were often 'illogical'. He would use words like 'because', 'then', 'however' and 'although' in ways which made the text at best unclear and at worst unintelligible.

In response to written tasks demanding an argument or discussion of issues, he would frequently produce a description. His sentences varied from the very short to the long, rambling over-complex type. There was a history of reading difficulties during primary school and his spelling was normal. His writing suggested a limited vocabulary, particularly through the extensive repetition of exact words in different sentences rather than using synonyms.

At this point in his school career Derek is taking a broad curriculum. Each school subject puts a different emphasis on language and faces Derek with a particular set of problems. We will consider these in turn, beginning with science.

A particular feature of science lessons at this point in the curriculum is the emphasis on space–time relations, with special emphasis on changing phenomena. Scientific textbooks and lessons are full of language which expresses spatial (more/less), temporal (when/then), causal (because/although) and conditional (only if/instead) relationships. These are expressed in ways which frequently use many of these terms in a single short text. For example:

> In certain parts of Australia crops grew very badly because there was no molybdenum in the soil. When the soil was sprayed with a very dilute solution of molybdenum the plants grew splendidly. Very little molybdenum was needed because too much of a trace element may have a damaging effect on plants.

Scientific language combines the interweaving of spatio-temporal relationships with a technical vocabulary. This vocabulary can either be using old words in new ways (e.g. 'energy') or new words with an unfamiliar look to them due to their classical origins (e.g. 'molecule').

Scientific language, then, whether being written, read or spoken, requires precision of vocabulary combined with recognition of the exact nature of the relationships expressed. It is not enough for the child to impose his own organisation onto scientific language. He must see what the language actually means. The level of precision required in the language of science puts considerable pressure on the skills of children like Derek.

The language of mathematics presents many similar problems to that of science. It uses relatively few words, phrases and sentences compared to other subjects, but these linguistic units carry a lot of precise information. Complex concepts and relationships are expressed in few words with little contextual information to help understanding. In fact, where contextual information is presented in mathematics it must often be treated in ways that differ from the real world as the child understands it. For example, simple arithmetic problems like 'If it takes two men three hours to dig a hole, how long does it take four men?' cannot be answered by enquiries into how strong the new men are, how many spades there are or do they spend more time talking or having tea-breaks.

Understanding the ground rules of applied mathematics problems requires an ability to take a non-literal perspective – a skill which many psychologists have suggested is at root based on mastery of the complex linguistic devices which children like Derek find difficult. The capacity to highlight, pick out or focus attention on different aspects of our experiences according to requirements is a crucial part of language use. It begins for normal children almost as soon as language is available to them. However, many language-disabled children lack the linguistic skill to change emphasis according to the social and congitive context. It is hard enough for them to say it one way adequately. The normal teenage child is able to linguistically put features of his world into foreground and/or background according to the requirements of the context. He knows that when the teacher is considering the mathematics of a projectile's motion a particular kind of idealised world is under consideration. This idealised world has become part of the conventions of the maths lesson. But it will have taken many hours of teacher talk over quite a long period to negotiate acceptance of this convention with the children. Once again the child with language difficulties is likely to be disadvantaged through failing to fully comprehend the process of negotiating these ground-rules for mathematical problem-solving.

A perhaps more obvious and equally important factor in undertanding difficulty in mathematics concerns the active rule of language in the process of solving Mathematical problems. Getting from the problem to the solution often involves a series of stages each involving syntactic (grammatical) and semantic (meaning) coding and recoding. We typically talk to ourselves often silently but also out loud, particulary when the going gets tough. This shows the importance of language to our mathematical thought processes. We will be dealing with complex transformations of data (e.g. to the nearest whole number) and specific terminology (e.g. polygon). Often these processes are tested at speed. Not surprisingly, language difficulties lead directly to poor mathematical performance, and children like Derek, whose basic problem is linguistic, are often thought of as having primary problems with mathematics. The crucial point is that when the extra appropriate language teaching is combined with care in the way lessons and problems are presented, Derek's performance will improve considerably.

We have referred so far to the language demands of science and mathematics. These curriculum areas are not always thought of as placing an emphasis on linguistic skill. More typically it is the arts and social sciences which are identified with literacy skills, and they do indeed require considerable sophistication in language use. At the grammatical level these subjects demand control of many of the most complex skills. Relative clause, conjunctions and 'wh' questions are mixed together with other forms of elaborate syntax. Narrative forms using subtle time markers together with difficult tense constructions are common. The semantics of this language relies on figurative language, comparisons and analogies. And many of the relationships expressed (e.g. causality) are implied rather than stated.

This complex language also places a considerable load on the attention and memory capacity of any child, especially those, like Derek, with language problems. From this very brief look at the language demands of the curriculum we can see that Derek is going to need considerable help with language of each school subject. He will need special help with the literacy skills (discussed in Ch. 9) as these relate to each subject. His teaching programme must focus on the language demands of each lesson and topic, never assuming that the words and phrases he could process previously have not been forgotten. Over a period of time a much clearer idea of the language demands of each lesson will be developed. A comprehensive set of worksheets and explanatory techniques to accompany the topics will be developed.

The resource implications of this approach to Derek's problems is clear, as is the speed at which Derek can progress through the curriculum. He will inevitably go somewhat slower, but surely this is preferable to understanding very little at a forced pace. But in Derek's case we are not suggesting an alternative curriculum; we are arguing for more support for him in his engagement with normal schooling.

However, some children's language problems are going to be such as to require more fundamental changes in the way they are taught. Consider the case of Susan, a 16-year-old girl whose spoken utterances are rarely more than two words long. Her paucity of language extends to her comprehension. She only seems to be able to focus on a small number of the words in any sentence; usually either the beginning or the end. As a result she fails to understand complex language.

Clearly, the language demands of the normal curriculum for a 16-year-old will be too taxing for Susan. In any case the interaction between language and cognitive development has slowed Susan's progress through school to the point where she is effectively functioning at an educational level which ranges from that of a 7 to 11-year-old, depending on the language demands of the task. Susan requires an individually tailored curriculum which plays to her strengths: perseverance and good visuo-spatial skills. Her programme must emphasise non-linguistic representation – drawings, pictures, films – relating these to real-life experiences, using visits and demonstrations. Language therapy should be interrelated with the curriculum modules, and as the SCORE model tells us, it should be taken into the content of Susan's visually oriented programme.

As we have already seen, many children's problems will fall between Derek's fairly minimal problems and Susan's extreme difficulties. Correspondingly, the extent to which children can deal with the normal curriculum will differ. There is no recipe which we can give to predict this in advance. Only careful assessment and observation will tell us enough about each child to provide a framework for curriculum planning. The message of this chapter is that in order to plan projects, we need to take account of the language demands of both what is taught and the way it is taught.

9

Reading, Writing and Language-Disabled Children: An Approach to Literacy

Very few schools do any formal teaching of reading or writing after children reach 10 years of age. Yet the demand for literacy skills increases dramatically as children get older. They are asked to express increasingly complex and abstract ideas in written form. Reading also increasingly becomes the source for the development of their understanding.

By the time children reach the age of 10, teachers assume they have mastery of reading skills. It is expected that they can skilfully operate the rules relating spoken to written language. General fluency with the visuo-spatial code of writing is expected to be not far behind those for the audio-temporal code of speech, at least at the word, phrase and sentence level. Of course, in many cases these expectations are realistic, although we would argue that secondary school teachers do sometimes overestimate the basic literacy skills of the children who first enter their schools. However, it is important to remember that as literacy becomes a more skilful activity, the graphic and phonic aspects become less important and the linguistic features become primary. Literacy increasingly depends on language skills and consequently presents a growing obstacle to the educational success of language-disabled children.

Despite these problems, we want to suggest that careful

consideration of the teaching of literacy can be turned to the advantage of language-disabled children; that through the medium of written language some of their problems can be reduced. We will do this using a framework for understanding literacy which is part of a more complex model of literacy skills developed by the Manchester University Literacy Project (directed by Mike Beveridge and Tom Christie with research fellows Pam Owen and Caroline Stainton; and funded by the Joint Matriculation Board). However, because the phonological aspects of language disability have implications for literacy, and this part of the model excludes phonology, we will look first at this issue.

As we have seen, some children have considerable difficulty developing a stable and consistent sound system for their language. For example, in English salient features of articulation such as voicing, place, manner and aspiration may not be perceived and organised into the English vowel and consonant system. Words will be mispronounced either consistently or inconsistently, often to such a degree as to make the child very difficult to understand (see Ch. 5, p. 37).

Learning how the sounds of a language correspond to the letters or letter combinations is a part of the process of beginning to read. If a child lacks a principled way of distinguishing the elements of the sound system, it will be very difficult for him to use this system as a basis for working out how letters relate to sounds. As we have discussed earlier, total absence of a sound system is rare, but many children have parts of their phonological system which is not fully or correctly formed. Common problems include confusion between *th* and *v* in words like 'with'; and difficulty with consonant clusters like *st* or *pr*; often only the first or last sound is pronounced in these clusters. Other typical patterns of error include (1) If there is more than one liquid or semi vowel (e.g. l, r, y, w) in a word, pronounce them all the same, – so words like 'wolf' become 'wowf'; and (2) 'Pronounce only the vowel sounds' – a strategy producing what is often referred to as open syllable speech.

Many children produce some aberrant speech for a period during language acquisition. But it is a passing phase for most of them – they soon grow out of it. However, language-disabled children may well carry these problems into the age range when they would normally be taught to read and write. This presents problems when we introduce these children to literacy. The sound system of a language forms the basis for most ways that children are taught to read. There is evidence that young children who can appreciate the sound problems of a language, even as detected on simple rhyming tasks, do better when they are taught to read. Children with phonological problems will find teaching methods based on sound/letter matching very difficult. How can we avoid this problem? On the one hand, we can try to avoid using the sound/letter matching process and instead emphasise the visual decoding of letters, what the letters look like, what words look like and relate them directly to meaning. In this way, we encourage the child to visually process printed words and directly relate them to their underlying meaning.

On the other hand, we suggest another solution can be found in the one basic principle which lies behind our model of literacy. This principle is that all reading and writing is the development of meaning in a communicative context. It is very easy to forget this because in the somewhat sterile conditions of most school writing there is only one person – the reader or writer – participating. The audience for most of what is written by school-children is a teacher sitting in judgement; and in many cases the only feedback the children get is a grade. This all too familiar situation causes many children to fail to appreciate the essentially communicative nature of reading and writing. This in turn means that they do not capitalise on the potential of reading and writing for developing their thinking skills.

Unfortunate though it is for children with no obvious language difficulties, they do at least have access to the social and educational world via talking and listening. However, our main concern here is the power of literacy to enhance the language skills of children with language disability. Writing is a permanent record of language which can be looked at, considered and altered to best fit the purposes it is supposed to serve. This process of reflecting on and changing language gradually builds up the child's skill in planning what to say, and successful planning means understanding the function the language serves. Literacy is particularly useful in developing planning skills, and we will now outline some of the different functions of written text which can form the basis of a teaching programme. These functions are analysis, argument, description, exposition, instruction and expression.

Analysis

The analytical function requires selection of content which enables reader and writer to *consider* issues. This content acts as a focus for deliberation and is used to *examine* specific aspects of the topic. The text is constructed to highlight *contrast* and the reader/writer is required to *evaluate*.

The following example is from a less able 16-year-old child's essay on the topic of his school's system of dealing with misbehaviour: 'The punishment does not always fit the crime because they give you detention. Sometimes they can't prove you have done anything. It's a load of rubbish.' The essay continues in this vein with little detailed information on the school punishment system. As a consequence, no *examination* of the facts appears; no *evaluation* of the good and bad points can be given.

We have found that teaching the child to plan the essay within an analytic framework will improve the quality considerably. Simple procedures like listing the good points and bad points separately, writing down why each point is good and then classifying these reasons, can give the child a way in to writing a satisfactory essay. These strategies can become second nature to the child in both the reading and writing role. For children with language disability the text can come to have some overall structure which helps to support their basic difficulties with language.

Argument

A text which is designed to function as an argument, selects its content in order to *persuade* the audience to support a pre-established point of view. The material is selected to *convince* and is organised to relate to this point of view, which is typically expressible in one or two sentences. The organisation of these texts requires that the relationship of *support* for the position is made as clearly as possible. This typically leads to some sentences functioning in a subordinate or supporting role to the points made in other sentences.

The following example is from a 14-year-old's essay on the positive value of comics: 'I buy comics. I like to start by getting number 1 and then I collect the comic. I don't buy Dandy or Beano very often.' Once again there is no real attempt to satisfy the text function demanded. There are a few facts about the child's own practices but no persuasive support for the argument is provided in the text. Clearly, the child needs to be taught about how to select the right content and how to categorise it according to the obvious criteria of pleasure, value for money, information, free gifts, and so on. Selecting the negative points of comics would be taught together with how to give reasons why these are not crucially problematic to the positive case being made. Language which helps this kind of text should be taught explicitly, for example, 'Some people who do not buy comics think that ... but ...'

Understanding these procedures together with the linguistic devices that go with argument will, once again, help the language-disabled child put together pieces of text successfully.

Description

The crucial aspect of describing is the process of *selecting* the appropriate characteristics of whatever is being described. Units of detail must be put together to give a picture of the whole. The content material is usually *concrete* rather than abstract. The organisational strategy required is usually that of linking through co-ordination. This is essentially an additive process which unlike argument or analysis does not require that the reader/writer draws the content together around one theme or to one conclusion.

The following example comes from a description of the life-cycle of the thrush by a 15-year-old: 'It has a big yellow beak and the mother waits for the baby to hatch. They have little speckles of black and the baby cannot fly until about two months old.' The co-ordination skills in this essay require adjustment. Facts are not linked in a way which allows the easiest transition from the topic of 'physical characteristics' to that of 'growth'. As before, prior classification of the content would help the organisation of the text.

Exposition

The main function of an expository text is to *interpret* and *explain*. This requires selecting and organising the content so that it becomes clear 'how or why things are as they are'. Reasons are given which relate one situation or stage in a process to another. This gives the text an *ordering* flavour, and the reader/writer is creating a sense of direction of events.

The following example is from a 15-year-old's exposition of the process of photosynthesis: 'A leaf contains chlorophyll, this makes them green. Leaves can make starch. This is photosynthesis and they also make sugar as well.' This text does not make it clear that the starch comes from sugars. The ordering of the content and the lack of cohesion produces a poor answer. As before, children should be taught to recognise the sequence of information which sets up the correct associations in the reader's mind. For example, an order such as (1) the process, (2) how do we identify, (3) how does it occur, (4) how important is it, will help the reader/writer get the right content in an intelligible order.

Instruction

The purpose of instructional texts is obviously to *regulate* behaviour. The content is selected to this end and focuses on stages in a process. In the text itself the connections between these stages need not be made explicit. The meaningful links in the text may be weak, the sense being derived from links to the common process being *directed*.

The following example comes from a 13-year-old's instructions to a friend who is taking over her paper delivering round: 'Then start off at the furthest away. Mr Jones will tie the dog up for you. On Wednesday a few people don't want papers. On Saturday you have to be careful at 7, Shady Lane

cos the twins attack you.' The major problem with this piece
is that it is more descriptive than instructive, a common error.
The organisational principle for content to be taught must
enable the child to select out and categorise the actions into
directions for walking, instructions at individual houses,
sorting procedures, daily variation, and so on. The text
structure can then be built around these preparatory
frameworks.

Expression

The content of expressive texts focuses on the reader/writer's
ability to *symbolise* or *represent* an experience. As with
analysis, *evaluation* is important in expressive texts, but in
this case the emphasis is on evaluation of feeling. Experiences
are presented as *imaginative* reconstructions with the purpose of inducing an affective response.

The following example comes from a 12-year-old's story
involving a family of American Indians: 'Kopi remembered
that his parents had died because he had not helped them. His
brothers told him to behave but he went away.' This extract
reveals the flavour of the whole text in that it fails to
represent the complexity of feelings that this situation
generates. It tends to concentrate on either the real events
which occur or make passing reference to emotional states.
The emotions of the characters are not used to give the reader
a sense of involvement in the story. We are left feeling
indifferent to the action.

As all teachers know, this type of writing is difficult to
encourage. It seems to stem as much from the involvement of
the writer with the story as it does from linguistic strategies.
But these involvements can be generated if the teacher can
excite the interest of pupils in understanding people through
language. This type of use of language is often thought to be
beyond the capacity of language-disabled pupils, but this is
not the case. Many quite severely language-disabled children
are easily drawn into narratives where the language is kept
simple but the emotional quality is high. People's feelings are
no less interesting to these children than others, and we
should not leave them with a literature which expresses

emotions at levels well beneath their capacity for understanding them.

The central point of this section is that language-disabled children can benefit from introducing literacy skills into their curriculum, and that even children with apparently severe sound/letter problems can benefit from this 'top down' approach when it is combined with other methods. We are not saying that reading and writing will solve their difficulties, but we do feel there is a tendency to treat the spoken word as if it were separate from literacy. We support the integration of text-based skills into the curriculum of children whose spoken language has problems. Furthermore, we would extend the range of language disabilities to include some of those children whose reading and writing skills remain poor after their initial problems with speech have apparently disappeared. The strategies outlined in this chapter are directed especially at this group of children.

Appendix:
Assessment Tools

A variety of tests and materials are available to professionals involved in assessing children's language. Many of these materials require some specialised knowledge of language development and linguistics. However, an increasing number of courses are available to teachers and other people with no such background in the use of tests and assessment materials and in the general principles of language development and linguistics. Thus there are now growing opportunities through in-service training to gain more in-depth knowledge about language.

The following is a brief review of the assessment tools available in Great Britain:

The Edinburgh Articulation Test (EAT) (Anthony, Bogle, Ingram and MacIsaacs, 1971) is a standardised test developed to assess 3 to 6-year-old children's phonology – that is, children's production of English consonant and consonant clusters. It was standardised in Edinburgh using 510 children and provides a way of comparing children's performance with that of other children of their own age. As mentioned in Chapter 5, the twenty six letters of the alphabet do not represent all the consonant sounds of English. This test does not therefore use alphabet letters to represent sounds but it uses phonetic symbols. Phonetic symbols are a useful tool for representing the sounds we need to speak. Thus it is a good idea to become acquainted with them if you have a child with phonological problems. This test will help you become familiar with about forty symbols which represent the sounds necessary to speak English.

This test though does not provide us with developmental guidelines as to which consonant contrasts are learned first and which are learned later. This information is of particular importance for planning a teaching programme. As we discussed in Chapter 4, the order principle suggests that we have some notion as to the order in which different language structures are learned. If we want to mimic normal language development, we need this information. Also, this test does not easily lend itself to the analysis of phonological processes – that is, which rules of speech is the child following. On the other hand, its qualitative analysis provides a useful way of checking a child's progress. And the quantitative analysis can give a quick comparison of children using the forty-one coloured pictures to elicit the child's language.

The Phonological Assessment of Child Speech (PACS) (Grunwell, 1985) is a diagnostic tool which analyses children's speech sound systems. It provides developmental information which allows the teacher/therapist (1) to compare the child's performance with that of children their own age as well as adults and (2) to design a phonological teaching programme based on the developmental order of acquisition. Use of the PACS requires knowledge of phonetic symbols.

The Reynell Developmental Language Scales, Second Revision (RDLS) (Reynell, 1979) is a standardised test which has two sections, one to assess expressive (speaking) language and the other to assess verbal comprehensive (listening and understanding) of children ranging in age from 1 to 7 years. In order to purchase the test, one needs to have speech therapy qualifications or have attended a course demonstrating its use. None the less, if your school has it, it is worth looking through it and, if interested, take a course on how to use it. The expressive scale is very general. It only taps certain aspects of expressive language, and at the sentence level it is not based on normal development. The verbal comprehension scales (there are two, A and B) are in wide use among speech therapists and other language professionals. The first section of these scales (up to item 7) provides useful information on the child's ability to name miniature objects, follow simple commands involving prepositions (in, on, under) and selecting minature toys by function (which one do we sweep the floor with?). The later sections, though, usually involve questions and commands with many information-carrying words. This makes it difficult to assess why the child failed to respond appropriately. Did the child fail to understand one of the information-carrying words or did he fail to understand more than one? Did the child fail because it was difficult to remember more than one information-carrying word? These are just a few of the possibilities. Once again, these sections do not appear to be developmentally motivated, and because of limited time they test a restricted set of language comprehension skills. None the less, this test is helpful in determing if indeed children are behind on their comprehension. Also it gives you an idea of what language comprehension entails (understanding words, sentences of different types, etc.).

The English Picture Vocabulary Tests (EPVT) (Brimer and Dunn, 1973) were developed to assess receptive vocabulary (understanding the meaning of words). Individual tests are available for the following age groups: 5:0 to 8:11, 7:0 to 11:11, 11:0 to 18:0 as well as a full-range test which covers children from 3 to 18 years of age. The full range of EPVT has not been fully standardised, which means that between-child comparisons on this test can be misleading.

British Picture Vocabulary Test (BPVS) (Dunn, Dunn, Whetton and Pintillie, 1982). This test has now largely superseded the earlier EPVT. It is fully standardised and there is no restriction on who can administer it. It covers the age range from 2:11 to 18:1 years of age. This test measures receptive vocabulary but does not provide guidelines for remediation in that the words tested do not give you clues as to what you need to work on if the child is to improve. If one finds that a child has poor vocabulary, the BPVS gives no clue as to where one could begin to improve it, thus making it difficult to follow the order principle in the SCORE model.

The Test of Reception of Grammar (TROG) (Bishop, 1982) is a standardised test for children ages 4 to 13 years, with no restrictions on who can administer it. It is quick and provides a tool for older school-age children. It allows the tester to ensure that the child knows the vocabulary used in the test items.

This test examines the child's ability to understand grammatical structures and contrasts such as plurals, negatives, adjectives, prepositions and relative clauses. The items are ordered in terms of grammatical complexity and thus are not fully based on normal language development because normal children do not always learn what is grammatically simplest first. Other factors such as conceptual/semantic complexity and parental input are also involved in learning different grammatical structures. This test, though, is very useful in assessing understanding of particular groups of grammatical structures.

The Sentence Comprehension Test (Wheldall, Hobsbaum and Mittler, 1979) is an example of the non-standardised assessment tools used by language professionals for describing child language. The test is available in an experimental version and can be purchased and administered by special language teachers as well as speech therapists. Do not let these restrictions put you off looking at the test. Most schools can make these materials available via the speech therapists or the language specialist. Examine the test and see if it is useful to you. If you think you would like to administer it, see what you need to do in order to qualify. Sometimes an in service evening course for a few weeks is all you need. It is useful for assessing children's comprehension of grammatical structures (past, future, comparatives, negatives etc.) and in this sense complements the TROG, which conveys many of the same structures but with older children (4–13 years).

The Symbolic Play Test (Lowe and Costello, 1976) in its experimental edition provides guidelines for assessing play in children 1 to 3 years of age. Miniature toys are presented to the child and he is allowed to play. The test is untimed and can be purchased and administered by speech therapists, psychologists and medical doctors with a background in developmental paediatrics. The strength of this test are the guidelines for observing child play, and these guidelines can be used when observing naturally occurring play, thus obviating the need for the specific miniature toys provided by the test and the test situation in general. Thus this test may be quite useful to teachers involved with young children or children with developmental handicaps. Once again, do not be put off by the purchasing and administering restrictions. They often sound worse than they are.

The Language Analysis, Remediation and Screening Procedure (LARSP) (Crystal, Fletcher and Garman, 1976) provides a method for describing and analysing children's utterances in terms of grammatical rules. It is one of a series of tools for describing child language developed by David Crystal and his colleagues at the University of Reading. It requires knowledge of linguistics to be able to classify utterances, and the process involved in the analysis is laborious and time-consuming. For example, you need to know which word in the sentence is a preposition, which is a noun, which is an adjective and which is a verb. You also need to know when the object of a sentence is direct and indirect, among other things. Many of the children with grammatical difficulties have specific problems with different parts of the utterance, so it is recommended that, as professionals interested in language disabilities, we develop our knowledge in this area. Teachers we have worked with have bought the book and, after getting over the initial shock of the terminology, have worked through much of it with the help of in-service courses and language specialists available at their school. This test is useful for charting early grammatical development (up to Stage IV, 2:6 to 3:0 years of age) and *does* provide developmentally based suggestions as to what the language-disabled child may need to work on next.

The Profile of Phonology (PROPH) (Crystal, 1982), another in the series of tests developed at Reading, provides a set of guidelines for the analysis of the sounds used by children when pronouncing words. The system is based on obtaining a sample of 100 different words from the child. This tool requires knowledge of phonetic symbols, which we discussed earlier in this section. It is rigid and very lengthy.

The Prosody Profile (PROP) (Crystal, 1982) complements the PROPH analysis by providing guidelines to classify the child's use of pitch, loudness, speed of speech, pause and rhythm. It requires knowledge of prosodic symbols and phonetic symbols. Prosodic symbols are symbols used to mark changes in intonation as we speak. This is probably the most difficult of all the profiles and the most specialised. The information provided is, in clinical terms, useful to only a handful of language-disabled children with intonation problems. Of course, such an analysis may be more relevant clinically for those with impaired hearing. Like the previous profiles, it is very time-consuming.

The Profile in Semantics (PRISM) (Crystal, 1982), again developed at Reading, is divided into two parts, one procedure is designed to classify the meanings conveyed by different grammatical elements in a sentence and the other is used to classify the child's inventory of words. This profile is the longest in paper (the chart has sixteen pages!), but again, working through it can provide one with insight as to how children convey meaning with words and combination of words.

David Ingram (1976) in Canada has developed a set of techniques to collect, examine and remediate the language of children with phonological problems. His book *Phonological Disability in Children*, provides useful discussions of different approaches to the analysis of language-disabled children's phonological system. The principles discussed can be applied in many different ways when examining phonologically disabled children. Reading and applying Ingram's techniques, like most tools related to phonology, requires familiarisation with phonetic symbols.

The Interpersonal Language Skills Assessment (ISLA): A Test of Pragmatic Behaviours (Blagden and McConnell, 1985) is available from Lingui Systems, Inc., 716 17th Street, Moline, Illinois, 61265, USA. In the area of conversational disability and pragmatics there is a dearth of assessment tools published (although many projects are under way), but the ISLA provides a framework for observing and categorising the social language skills of children 8 to 14 years of age while they interact with their peers. It also provides standardised information which allows the professional to identify patterns of behaviour which may lead to social alienation and conversational disability in children. It requires the person administering the test, to tape or video record a fifteen or twenty-minute sample of peer interaction. This sample forms the basis from which an analysis is carried out and patterns of behaviours are identified. The major behaviours classified are advising/predicting, commanding, commenting, criticising, informing, justifying, requesting and supporting. It has clear guidelines with examples which facilitate classification, and it provides a useful tool for assessing social and conversational disabilities.

The Portage Guide to Early Education(Shearer and Shearer, 1976) and *The PIP Development Charts* (Jeffree and McConkey, 1976) are among the published checklists which provide developmental guidelines on language and other areas such as motor abilities and self-help skills. It is probably true to say that every health authority develops their own checklist in addition to using what is already available.

In addition to the instruments described here, there is an abundance of research on normal and impaired language development from which language professionals draw useful diagnostic and remedial information. The modern teacher needs to be a well-informed, keen observer and experimenter as well as a test administrator.

In order to obtain additional information on British and American Assessment and remediation instruments for pre-school and school-age children please write to (1) NFER-Nelson Publishing Company, Darville House, 2 Oxford Road East, Windsor, Berks SL4 1DF, (2) The Test Agency, Cournswood House, North Dean, High Wycombe, Bucks HP14 4NW, and (3) The National College of Speech Sciences, Test Library Catalogue, 84A Heath Street, Hampstead, London NW3 1DN.

Further Reading

Anthony, A., Bogle, B., Ingram, T.T.S. and McIsaacs, M.W. (1971). *The Edinburgh Articulation Test (EAT)* Edinburgh, E. and S. Livingstone.

Bangs, T. E. (1982). *Language and Learning Disorders of the Pre-academic Child*. Englewood Cliffs, NJ, Prentice Hall.

Bishop, D. (1982). *The Test of Reception of Grammar (TROG)*. Available from the author, Psychology Department, University of Manchester.

Blagden, C.M. and McConnell, N.L. (1985). *The Interpersonal Language Skills Assessment (ISLA): A Test of Pragmatic Behaviour*. Moline, Ill., Lingui Systems.

Bloom, L. & Lahey, M. (1978). *Language Development and Language Disorders*. New York, John Wiley & Sons.

Brimer, A. and Dunn, L. (1973). *The English Picture Vocabulary Test (EPUT)*. Newham, Gloucestershire, Educational Evaluation Enterprises.

Carrow-Woolfolk, E. and Lynch, J. (1981). *An Integrative Approach to Language Disorders in Children*. London, Academic Press.

Cole, P.R. (1982) *Language Disorders in Pre-school Children*. Englewood Cliffs, NJ, Prentice Hall.

Crystal, D., Fletcher, P. and Garman, M. (1976). *The Grammatical Analysis of Language Disability: A Procedure for Assessment and Remediation*. London, Edward Arnold.

(1979). *Working with LARSP*. London, Edward Arnold.

(1982). *Profiling Linguistic Disability*. London, Edward Arnold.

Dunn, L.M., Dunn, L.M., Whetton, C. and Pintillie, D. (1982). *British Picture Vocabulary Test*. Windsor, NFER-Nelson.

Elliot, C., Murray, D.J. and Pearson, L.S. (1983). *The British Ability Scales*. Windsor, NFER-Nelson.

Gallagher, T. and Prutting, C. (1983). *Pragmatic Assessment and Intervention Issues in Language*. London, Taylor and Francis.

Grunwell, P. (1985). *Phonological Assessment of Child Speech*. Windsor, NFER-Nelson.

Habbuck, R.D. (1981). *Children's Language Disorders*. Englewood Cliffs, NJ, Prentice Hall.

Hastings, P. and Hayes, B. (1981). *Encouraging Language Development*. London, Croom Helm.

Hutt, E. (1986). *Teaching Language-Disordered Children: A Structured Curriculum*. London, Edward Arnold.

Ingram, D. (1976). *Phonological Disability in Children*. London, Edward Arnold.

Jeffree, D.M. and McConkey, R. (1976). *The PIP Developmental Charts*. Sevenoaks, Hodder and Stoughton.

Lahey, M. (1988). *Language Disorders and Language Development*. London, Collier MacMillan Publishers.

Lowe, M. and Costello, A. (1977). *Symbolic Play Test*. Windsor, NFER-Nelson.

Miller, J.F. (1981). *Assessing Language Production in Children*. Baltimore, Md, University Park Press.

Nolan, M. and Tucker, I.G. (1981). *The Hearing Impaired Child and His Family*. London, Souvenir Press.

Piaget, J. (1950). *The Nature of Intelligence*. London: Routledge & Kegan Paul.

Reynell, J. (1979). *Reynell Developmental Language Scale (Second Revision)*. Windsor, NFER-Nelson.

Ripich, D.N. and Spinelli, F.M. (1985). *School Discourse Problems*. London, Taylor and Francis.

Shames, G.H. and Rubin, H. (1986). *Stuttering Then and Now*. London, Merrill.

Schiefelbusch, R.L. (1986). *Language Competence: Assessment and Intervention*. London, Taylor and Francis.

Schiefelbusch, R.L. and Pickar, J. (1984). *The Acquisition of Communicative Competence*. Baltimore, Md, University Park Press.

Shearer, D.E. and Shearer, M.S. (1976). 'The Portage Project: A Model for Early Childhood Intervention', in T.J. Tjossem (ed.), *Intervention Strategies for High Risk Infants and Young Children*, Baltimore, Md, University Park Press. The Portage Project Instructional Programme is available from NFER-Nelson.

Simon, C.S. (1985a). *Communication Skills and Classroom Success: Therapy Methodologies for Language-Learning Disabled Students*. London, Taylor and Francis.

(1985b). *Communication Skills and Classroom Success: Assessment of Language-Learning Disabled Students*. London, Taylor and Francis.

Stubbs, M. (1983). *Language, Schools and Classrooms*. London, Methuen.

Tizard, B. and Hughes, M. (1984). *Young Children Learning*. London, Fontana Paperbacks.

Van Riper, C. (1982). *The Nature of Stuttering*. London, Prentice Hall.

Wallach, G.P. and Butler, K.G. (1984). *Language Learning Disabilities in School-Age Children*. London, Williams and Wilkins.

Warner, J.A.W., Byers-Brown, B. and McCartney, E. (1984). *Speech Therapy: A Clinical Campanion*. Manchester, Manchester University Press.

Wells, G. (1981). *Learning Through Interaction: The Study of Language Development*. Cambridge, Cambridge University Press.

(1985), *Language Development in the Pre-school Years*. Cambridge, Cambridge, Cambridge University Press.

Whedall, K., Hobsbaum, A. and Mittler, P. (1979). *The Sentence Comprehension Test*. Windsor, NFER-Nelson.

Wiig, E.H. and Semel, E.M. (1984). *Language Assessment and Intervention for the Learning Disabled (Second Edition)*. Colombus, Ohio, Charles E. Merrill.

Winitz, H. (1983). *Treating Language Disorders*. Baltimore Md, University Park Press.

Wood, M.L. (1982). *Language Disorders in School-Age Children*. Englewood Cliffs, NJ, Prentice Hall.

Index